MY DAILY *Prayer* JOURNAL

WITH INSIGHTS BY

BILLY GRAHAM

My Daily Prayer Journal
With Insights by Billy Graham

Paperback Edition
©2007, revised 2008 Billy Graham Evangelistic Association

Grason is the literature ministry of the Billy Graham Evangelistic Association.

ISBN: 978-1-59328-228-8

Contents

Think Back to your own childhood for a moment. When you were young, did you talk with your father in a series of carefully memorized sentences? No, of course not. You talked with him freely and openly about everything—and he delighted in that. The same is true with God, your Heavenly Father. He delights in the prayers of His people! Don't worry whether you're eloquent enough; your father didn't turn you away when you spoke baby talk—and neither does God.

—BILLY GRAHAM

How to Use This Journal

THIS FRESH AND USABLE JOURNAL is specially designed to help you develop a personal prayer plan and keep track of your prayer life. Billy Graham's insights on prayer are found throughout, along with other prayer helps.

START ANY TIME OF THE YEAR

There is space to record your prayer concerns for one year, and you can begin any time of the year. Start today on pages 18–19 and continue for the next 52 weeks.

Remember the recommendation that a regular daily prayer time may be better, even if it is short, than waiting for occasional longer times to pray. This journal also provides a daily place to record the answers you receive to your prayers. By noting key things you pray from day to day, and the date, you will become more aware of the different ways God may be answering those prayers.

Sample journal entry

SUNDAY
Pray from Matthew 1

Prayer Concerns

- need to get along better with friends at church
- concerned about what kids learning at school
- budget getting tight

Answers

- had helpful conversation
- talked with Johnny—he sees the problem
- found some places to cut

CONVERSATION STARTER

Notice the suggested Scripture reading for each day, which will take you through the entire New Testament in a year. Prayer is conversation with God, and as you read these passages you can think of them as "conversation openers" between you and God. Let Him first speak to you through His Word, then spend time with Him in prayer. Many days, if you are alert, the Holy Spirit will use your Bible reading to suggest something He wants you to pray.

Find encouraging insights on page 49 about how to pray the words of Scripture.

GOD'S OWN PRAYER REQUEST

Finally, remember God's own request to pray for the nations. Make this a weekly part of your prayer life, because doing so is very pleasing to God. Find out how on page 23.

May God bless you as you faithfully seek Him.

Remember that *God Helps* us when we pray. ... This is a mystery we will never fully understand this side of Heaven— but it also is a great comfort. The Bible says, *"The Spirit helps us in our weakness. We do not know what we ought to pray for, but the Spirit himself intercedes for us with groans that words cannot express"* (see Romans 8:26). ... That *"the Spirit himself intercedes"* indicates that it is actually God pleading, praying, and mourning through us. Thus we become co-laborers with God, actual partners with Him; our lives are lifted from the low plane of selfishness to the high plane of creativeness with God.

—BILLY GRAHAM

Prayer

BY BILLY GRAHAM

God Himself is the power that makes prayer work. Find out how you can pray more effectively and receive the answers to prayer that only God can give.

THE MEN UPON WHOSE SHOULDERS RESTED the initial responsibility of Christianizing the world came to Jesus with one supreme request. They did not say, "Lord, teach us to preach"; "Lord, teach us to do miracles"; or "Lord, teach us to be wise" ... but they said, "Lord, teach us to pray."

No one has given more encouragement to praying than did Jesus. The followers of Christ were both encouraged to pray and taught how to pray. They saw constantly the example He set in praying, and they noted the direct relationship between Jesus' unusual ministry and His devout life of prayer.

Jesus considered prayer more important than food, for the Bible says that hours before breakfast, "*In the morning, having risen a long while before daylight, He went out and departed to a solitary place; and there He prayed*" (Mark 1:35, NKJV).

To the Son of God prayer was more important than the assembling of great throngs. The Bible says, "*And great multitudes came together to hear, and to be healed by Him of their infirmities. So He Himself often withdrew into the wilderness and prayed*" (Luke 5:15–16, NKJV).

The precious hours of fellowship with His Heavenly Father meant more to our Savior than sleep, for the Bible says, "*Now it came to pass in those days that He went out to the mountain to pray, and continued all night in prayer to God*" (Luke 6:12, NKJV).

He prayed at funerals, and the dead were raised. He prayed over the five loaves and two fishes, and a multitude were fed with a little boy's lunch. He prayed, "Not My will, but Yours," and a way was made whereby sinful men and women might approach a holy God.

> IT PLEASES GOD TO RELATE HIS WORK IN THE WORLD TO THE PRAYERS OF HIS PEOPLE.

It pleased God to relate His work in the world to the prayers of His people. Noah prayed, and God handed him a blueprint of the ark of deliverance. Moses prayed, and God delivered the Israelites from Egyptian bondage. Gideon prayed, and the host of a formidable enemy fled in fear before his valiant, prayerful 300. Daniel prayed, and the mouths of the lions were closed. Elijah prayed, and the fire of God consumed the sacrifice and licked up the water around the altar. David prayed, and he defeated Goliath on the Philistine battleground.

The disciples prayed, and they were filled with the Holy Spirit so that 3,000 were added to the church in one day. Paul prayed, and hundreds of churches were born in Asia Minor and Europe. God does answer prayer.

AVOID SHORT-CIRCUITING

Some prayers are answered with a "yes" and some with a "no." But what about unanswered prayer?

Perhaps your prayers have been mingled with doubts. Perhaps you have prayed selfishly. Perhaps you have asked God for things which were not best for you. "I prayed earnestly and nothing happened," many will say in a tone of dismay. "I asked for guidance, and I'm in serious trouble" … "I asked God for a companion, and I have found no one" … "I asked God for a good home, and look at the misery and confusion in our house."

The Bible says that there are specific reasons why prayers are not answered.

It may be that your prayers are not answered because of disobedience. A disobedient son cannot expect to "have his cake and eat it too," as we say. The Bible says, "*If you do not obey the voice of the Lord your God, to observe carefully all His commandments and His statutes which I command you today, that all these curses will come upon you and overtake you*" (Deuteronomy 28:15, NKJV).

Perhaps your prayers are not answered because of secret sin. David said (and he should know), "*If I had cherished sin in my heart, the Lord would not have listened*" (Psalm 66:18). Sin short-circuits the communication system between earth and heaven, and your praying with an evil heart will not even reach God.

Another reason for prayers not being answered is selfishness or willfulness. The Bible says, "*When you ask, you do not receive, because you ask with wrong motives, that you may spend what you get on your pleasures*" (James 4:3). Prayer serves a dual purpose: the blessing of man and the glory of God. If a prayer is prayed willfully for our own benefit but not for God's glory, it's not worthy of being answered. "Not my will, but Yours, be done" (see Luke 22:42) is the spirit of effectual prayer.

Real prayer is not a vain repetition of words uttered in public for religious display. Jesus said, "*And when you pray, do not be like the hypocrites, for they love to pray standing in the synagogues and on the street corners to be seen by men. I tell you the truth, they have received their reward in full*" (Matthew 6:5).

Prayer, in the true sense, is not a futile cry of desperation born of fear or frustration. Thousands of people pray only when they are under great stress, or in danger, overcome by uncertainty. I have been in airplanes when an engine died; then people started praying. We have flown through bad thunderstorms when people who may never have thought to pray before were praying all around us. I have talked to soldiers who told me that they never prayed until they were in the midst of battle. There seems to be an instinct in people to pray in times of trouble.

We know "there are no atheists in foxholes," but the kind of Christianity that fails to reach into our everyday lives will never change the world.

Prayer is not limited to conventional religious postures; nor is it restricted to houses of worship or religious ceremony. The Bible says, "*I want men everywhere to lift up holy hands in prayer, without anger or disputing*" (1 Timothy 2:8).

When you pray, your physical posture is not so important as the attitude of your heart. Many people put a great deal of emphasis on the position of the body during prayer. Some groups or sects insist that you kneel every time you pray or that you fold your hands in a certain way. All of this is relatively unimportant, though kneeling is an act of humility when sincerely done.

VERY FEW OF US HAVE LEARNED HOW TO FULLY DEVELOP THE POWER OF PRAYER.

PRAY IN STEP WITH GOD

Praying is simply a two-way conversation between you and God. The reason many of the great saints have closed their eyes while praying is to shut out the affairs of the world so that their minds could be completely concentrated on their conversations with God. However, nowhere in Scripture does it say that even the closing of the eyes is important, though it certainly lends itself to the attitude of prayer.

The next question many ask is: "Who is told to pray?" Scripture gives the answer, "All men."

Again, many ask: "Where are we commanded to pray?" Paul gives us the answer when he says, "Everywhere."

Some may also ask, "When are we told to pray?" The Scripture says, "Always." It is a command, a duty, and a privilege. In this modern age in which we live, we have learned to harness the power of the mighty Niagara and turn its force to our use and our good. We have learned to hold steam captive in boilers, and release its tremendous power to turn our machines. We have learned how to contain gasoline vapors in a cylinder, and explode them at the appointed second to move our automobiles and trucks quickly along our highways. We have even discovered the secret of releasing energy in the atom, which is capable of destroying entire cities and civilizations.

But very few of us have learned how to fully develop the power of prayer. We have not yet learned that men and women are more powerful when they are in prayer than when they are behind the most powerful guns we have ever developed. We have not learned that a nation is more powerful when it unites in earnest prayer than when its resources are channeled into defensive weapons. We have not discovered that the answers to all our problems can be had through contact with Almighty God.

GOD HIMSELF IS THE POWER THAT MAKES PRAYER WORK.

Scores of missionaries, in all parts of the world, have told me, "Please get the people back home to pray for us. We would rather have their prayers than anything else." If the Christians back home realized how much their prayers meant to these valiant heroes of the faith, they would not cease to pray day and night for their representatives out there in foreign mission fields.

Christian workers here at home also need your prayers. I know from personal experience. We are only able to move forward in our evangelistic work—the Crusades, the film ministry, television, radio, and Internet—by your prayers. If it were not for the prayers of thousands of God's people throughout the world, our ministry would completely fail.

APPROACH THE THRONE OF GOD

Now let us look at prayer objectively. What does the Bible say about effectual praying?

First: PRAYER IS FOR GOD'S CHILDREN.

Jesus said, "When you pray, say, Our Father ..." (see Matthew 6:9).

God has a particular responsibility to His children; and unless we have been born into the family of God through the new birth, we have no right to ask favors of God. The Bible says, *"But as many as received Him, to them He gave the right to become children of God, to those who believe in His name"* (John 1:12, NKJV).

I have had new Christians say to me, "I don't know how to pray. I don't have the right words."

When our children were just learning to talk and had difficulty finding the right words, they still managed to make themselves understood to my wife and me, and the mistakes they made only endeared them to us. In fact, I am sure I treasure their early attempts at conversation more than the words of most adults speaking without hesitation and without error.

My friend, if your prayers have not been answered, God invites you to the intimacy of spiritual sonship, *"that you may become blameless and pure, children of God without fault in a crooked and depraved generation, in which you shine like stars in the universe"* (Philippians 2:15).

Second: EFFECTUAL PRAYER IS OFFERED IN FAITH.

The Bible says, "*Therefore I tell you, whatever you ask for in prayer, believe that you have received it, and it will be yours*" (Mark 11:24).

Maltbie Babcock said, "Our prayers are to mean something to us if they are to mean anything to God." It goes without saying that if our prayers are aimless, meaningless, and mingled with doubt, they will go unanswered. Prayer is more than a wish turned heavenward ... it is the voice of faith directed Godward.

Third: DYNAMIC PRAYER EMANATES FROM AN OBEDIENT HEART.

The Bible says, "*And whatever we ask we receive from Him, because we keep His commandments and do those things that are pleasing in His sight*" (1 John 3:22, NKJV).

I know a wealthy father who refused to get his son a bicycle because the boy's report card showed disgracefully low marks, a yard remained unraked, and other assignments had not been carried out. I am sure the father would not have been wise to lavish gifts upon such a disobedient and ungrateful son.

The Bible says, "*However, if you do not obey the voice of the Lord, but rebel against the commandment of the Lord, then the hand of the Lord will be against you*" (1 Samuel 12:15, NKJV).

If you want to get your prayers through to God, surrender your stubborn will to Him, and He will hear your cry. Obedience is the master key to effectual prayer.

Fourth: WE ARE TO PRAY IN CHRIST'S NAME.

Jesus said, "*And whatever you ask in My name, that I will do, that the Father may be glorified in the Son*" (John 14:13, NKJV).

We are not worthy to approach the holy throne of God except through our Advocate, Jesus Christ.

The Bible says, "*Seeing then that we have a great High Priest who has passed through the heavens, Jesus the Son of God ... let us therefore come boldly to the throne of grace*" (Hebrews 4:14, 16, NKJV).

> OBEDIENCE IS THE MASTER KEY TO EFFECTUAL PRAYER.

God, for Christ's sake, forgives our sins. God, for Christ's sake, supplies our needs. God, for Christ's sake, receives our prayers. The person who comes with confidence to the throne of grace has seen that his approach to God has been made possible because of Jesus Christ.

Many may ask, "Is there no other way to pray except through Jesus Christ?" You may pray, but according to the Bible, "*There is ... one mediator between God and men, the man Christ Jesus*" (1 Timothy 2:5).

Fifth: WE MUST DESIRE THE WILL OF GOD.

Even our Lord, contrary to His own disposition at the moment, said, *"O My Father, if this cup cannot pass away from Me unless I drink it, Your will be done"* (Matthew 26:42, NKJV).

Prayer couples you with God's true purposes for you and the world. It not only brings the blessings of God's will to your own personal life, but it brings you the added blessing of being in step with God's plan.

And last: OUR PRAYER MUST BE FOR GOD'S GLORY.

The model prayer which Jesus has given us concludes with, *"Yours is the kingdom and the power and the glory forever"* (Matthew 6:13, NKJV). If we are to have our prayers answered, we must give God the glory. Our Lord said to His disciples, *"And whatever you ask in My name, that I will do, that the Father may be glorified in the Son"* (John 14:13, NKJV).

What a privilege is ours: the privilege of prayer! Christian, examine your heart, reconsecrate your life, yield yourself to God unreservedly, for only those who pray through a clean heart will be heard by Him. The Bible says, *"The prayer of a righteous man is powerful and effective"* (James 5:16).

We are to pray in times of adversity, lest we become faithless and unbelieving. We are to pray in times of prosperity, lest we become boastful and proud.

We are to pray in times of danger, lest we become fearful and doubting. We need to pray in times of security, lest we become self-sufficient. Sinners, pray to a merciful God for forgiveness! Christians, pray for an outpouring of God's Spirit upon a willful, evil, unrepentant world. Parents, pray that God may crown your home with grace and mercy! Children, pray for the salvation of your parents!

Christians, saints of God, pray that the dew of Heaven may fall on earth's dry, thirsty ground, and that righteousness may cover the earth as the waters cover the sea. Pray, believing, with this promise of our Savior in mind, *"Whatever you ask for in prayer, believe that you have received it, and it will be yours"* (Mark 11:24).

"Satan trembles when he sees the weakest saint upon his knees"—so pray, Christian, pray!

Have a Vital Time Alone With God

BY BILLY GRAHAM

SEVERAL PRACTICAL GUIDELINES have been helpful to me in maintaining a vital and regular time alone with God.

FIRST, set aside time each day to spend time with God. It may be early in the morning, or at least before you begin the day's regular activities. Make it a time when you are mentally alert, when you have no distractions, and you are not rushed. Discipline yourself to keep this time every day, even when travel or a busy schedule makes it difficult. Make it such a regular part of your life that you would no more skip it than you would miss eating a meal.

SECOND, come with a spirit of expectancy and obedience. Expect God to meet you through His Word, and tell Him that you want to be taught by Him. Come with a willingness to hear His Word and then to obey it. Remember: God the Holy Spirit has inspired the Bible, and we must look expectantly to Him to illumine our understanding of it.

> PRAY ABOUT THE PASSAGE OF SCRIPTURE YOU HAVE JUST READ.

THIRD, read through the Bible systematically. It is far too easy to dwell only on familiar passages, or skip around almost at random finding passages that happen to appeal to us. But we need to understand "*the whole counsel of God*" (Acts 20:27, RSV), and we need therefore to read and study every part of the Bible. Some people find it helpful to have a plan by which they will cover the entire Bible in a year.

FOURTH, read thoughtfully and prayerfully, and then meditate on what you have read. Some people pride themselves on covering a set number of chapters each day— but have no idea what they have read when they are finished! In his helpful, little booklet "Manna in the Morning" Dr. Stephen F. Olford wrote, "Read the portion at least three times. Read it carefully to discover what is there generally. The next time, peruse it for what is there specially. Then study it for what is there personally. ... [Then] say: 'Lord, as I look at this passage this morning, is there any command to obey? Is there any promise to claim? Is there any new thought to follow and pursue? Is there any sin to avoid? Is there any new thought about God? About the Lord Jesus? About the Holy Spirit? About the devil?' Seek to discover what God is saying to you from the passage you have read."

FIFTH, make prayer a central part of your time with God. In our Bible study, God speaks to us; in our prayer times, we speak to God. Make prayer first of all a time of praise and thanksgiving. Then pray about the passage of Scripture you have just read, asking Him to show you specific ways that it applies to your life. In addition, confess your sins to God. Finally, bring before God your own needs and the needs of others. Many people find it helpful to keep a prayer diary, in which they list those for whom they are praying and note God's specific answers.

FINALLY, put what you have learned into action, and walk with Christ every minute of the day. Perhaps God has been speaking to you in your quiet time about your relationship with someone in your family or a co-worker. Commit that situation into His hands—and then move forward in obedience and faith, knowing that the Holy Spirit will help you as you seek to have a right relationship with that person.

MANY PEOPLE FIND IT USEFUL TO KEEP A PRAYER DIARY, IN WHICH THEY LIST THOSE FOR WHOM THEY ARE PRAYING AND NOTE GOD'S SPECIFIC ANSWERS.

A Weekly Prayer Strategy

MONDAY—FAMILY

❋ Pray for immediate family members. (You may want to get actual requests from them individually.)

❋ Pray for friends of family members.

TUESDAY—CHURCH

❋ Pray for the leadership in your local fellowship.

❋ Pray for the marriages and families of your church leadership; they are key targets of Satan.

❋ Pray for specific ministries within your church.

WEDNESDAY—COMMUNITY

❋ Pray for community leaders.

❋ Pray for the churches in your community.

❋ Pray for Christian endeavors in your community (e.g., evangelism outreaches, pro-life efforts, ministries to the homeless, etc.).

THURSDAY—NATION

❋ Pray for our president.

❋ Pray for elected officials from your state.

❋ Pray for the seminaries that are training our future pastors and Christian leaders.

FRIDAY—WORLD

❋ Pray for world peace.

❋ Pray for the missionaries your church supports.

❋ Pray for individual nations of the world. (See specific prayer suggestions throughout this journal, beginning on page 23.)

SATURDAY—AFFLICTED

❋ Pray for those ministering in difficult circumstances in developing countries.

❋ Pray for those in prison.

❋ Pray for those from your church who are hospitalized or sick.

❋ Pray for the children affected by divorce.

Almost *Every Week*, I get at least one letter from someone who has prayed for a loved one for many years without any apparent effect. And yet they go on to say that their prayers finally have been answered. In other words, if God has put a burden on your heart for an unbelieving loved one, keep on praying for her. Remember: You may be the only person on earth who is still praying for that person—and that is an awesome responsibility.

—BILLY GRAHAM

Practical Prayer Suggestions

BASED ON MR. GRAHAM'S TEACHING

Five Practical Steps to Encourage You in Prayer

1. DESIRE THE WILL OF GOD

Jesus taught us to pray, "Your will be done." The key is not the words, but your attitude. Seek God's will and God's best for whatever you are praying about. He may respond in unexpected ways that please Him and will delight you. *"Your will be done on earth as it is in heaven"* (Matthew 6:10).

2. SEARCH YOUR HEART

God may not respond when you allow sin to remain in your life. If so, don't stop praying. Rather, confess your sins or wrong motives to God. He already knows your heart. God has promised always to respond to that prayer (see 1 John 1:9). *"If I had cherished sin in my heart, the Lord would not have listened"* (Psalm 66:18).

3. PRAY IN FAITH

Express your requests freely to God in childlike faith. As a child who trusts a wise and loving parent, ask in complete faith that He is able to do whatever you ask and that He will know what is best.

"The prayer of a righteous man is powerful and effective. Elijah was a man just like us. He prayed earnestly that it would not rain, and it did not rain on the land for three and a half years. Again he prayed, and the heavens gave rain, and the earth produced its crops" (James 5:16–18).

4. PRAY EVERY DAY

God wants to hear from you regularly. He wants a relationship. Take time to talk to God daily and throughout the day, not just when you face a crisis and not only with a list of wants and needs. *"Pray continually"* (1 Thessalonians 5:17).

5. PRAY FOR GOD'S GLORY

Pray for things to happen in such a way as to provide God with the credit and to give God the glory. He is powerful, magnificent, and majestic. And He is still our closest, most intimate Friend. Praise Him and ask for things that matter to Him. *"To the only wise God be glory forever through Jesus Christ! Amen"* (Romans 16:27).

Rejoice in the *Lord* always. … Let your
gentleness be evident to all. … In everything, by prayer
and petition, with thanksgiving, present your requests
to God. And the peace of God, which transcends all
understanding, will guard your hearts and your
minds in Christ Jesus.

—PHILIPPIANS 4:4—7

SUNDAY
Pray from Matthew 1

Prayer Concerns   *Answers*

MONDAY
Matthew 2

TUESDAY
Matthew 3

WEDNESDAY

Matthew 4

THURSDAY

Matthew 5:1–26

FRIDAY

Matthew 5:27–48

SATURDAY

Matthew 6:1–18

Happy is the man who has learned the secret of coming to God in daily prayer. Even 15 minutes alone with God every morning before you start the day can change circumstances and remove mountains!

—BILLY GRAHAM

One day *Jesus* was praying in a certain place. When he finished, one of his disciples said to him, "Lord, teach us to pray ... ." He said to them, "When you pray, say: 'Father, hallowed be your name, your kingdom come.'"

—LUKE 11:1—2

SUNDAY
Pray from Matthew 6:19–34

Prayer Concerns   *Answers*

MONDAY
Matthew 7

TUESDAY
Matthew 8:1–17

HOW TO PRAY FROM SCRIPTURE, SEE PAGE 49

WEDNESDAY
Matthew 8:18–34

Prayer Concerns   *Answers*

THURSDAY
Matthew 9:1–17

FRIDAY
Matthew 9:18–38

SATURDAY
Matthew 10:1–20

The men upon whose shoulders rested the initial responsibility of Christianizing the world came to Jesus with one supreme request. They did not say, "Lord, teach us to preach"; "Lord, teach us to do miracles"; or "Lord, teach us to be wise" ... but they said, "Lord, teach us to pray."

—BILLY GRAHAM

Pray for our *World* and its leaders every day—beginning now. Yes, you may wonder exactly what good prayers like this are accomplishing because our world has so many problems—and they never seem to get any better. But listen: Have you ever asked yourself how much worse off the world might be if God's people didn't pray? Only in eternity will we know the full impact of our prayers.

—BILLY GRAHAM

Praying for the Nations

GOD'S OWN PRAYER REQUEST

"Only ask, and I will give you the nations as your inheritance."

—Psalm 2:8 (NLT)

While praying for our own requests, do we give time to praying what God has requested? The Father's plan is to give the nations to the Son (see Psalm 2:7–8). As children of the Father and co-heirs with Christ (see Romans 8:17), we have a stake in this plan. Because it is the Father's request that we **ask** for the nations, *My Daily Prayer Journal* includes a special feature to help you pray for people nation by nation.

A NATION A WEEK

Every country in the world is listed in this journal. Interspersed throughout this journal are brief reports on 52 of those countries along with a suggestion on how and what to pray for the people of that specific nation. All remaining countries are listed on pages 156–157.

God is passionate about the people of the nations; use *My Daily Prayer Journal* to help you participate in His passion.

PRAYING GOD'S REQUEST

When praying for the nations, you may wish to pray based on words of Scripture:

"All the ends of the earth
will remember and turn to the Lord,
and all the families of the nations
will bow down before him,
for dominion belongs to the Lord
and he rules over the nations" (Psalm 22:27–28).

"This is what is written: ... repentance and forgiveness of sins
will be preached in his name to all nations" (Luke 24:46–47).

Pray for Argentina

Unlike many Latin American countries, Argentina has a distinctly European heritage. Most Argentines are direct descendants of Italian, Spanish, French, and German immigrants. The nation is nominally Roman Catholic, but evangelical Protestant churches and charismatic-influenced Catholic groups are growing rapidly. Following a nationwide outreach led cooperatively by the Billy Graham Evangelistic Association and 8,000 Argentine churches, 27,000 new believers were baptized a few years ago by local churches across the nation in a single day. **PRAY** for these new Christians to continue to grow in faith, as well as for thousands of others who made decisions for Christ during the same time period. *See Acts 2:41–42*

Population: 39,921,833
Capital: Buenos Aires
Languages: Spanish, English
Literacy: 96%
Income (GDP) per capita: $13,700
Religions: Roman Catholic 90%,
evangelical Protestant 6%, Jewish and other 4%

Armenia

In 301 AD, Armenia became the first country in history to adopt Christianity as its state religion. The Armenian Apostolic Church continues to this day. Armenia emerged from 70 years of Soviet Communist domination in 1991 and is now a Christian country largely surrounded by Islam. Armenians overwhelmingly profess Christianity as their religion, but many see this as a patriotic distinctive instead of a relationship with Christ. **PRAY** that God will awaken the hearts of those who are religious but do not know Christ personally. *See Ephesians 5:14*

Population: 2,976,372
Capital: Yerevan
Language: Armenian
Literacy: 99%
Income (GDP) per capita: $5,300
Religions: Armenian Apostolic 95%,
other Christian 4%, other 1%

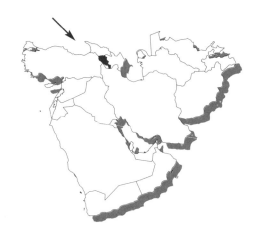

AUSTRALIA

Australia is generally regarded as one of the more secular nations in the world, and increasing numbers of Australians identify themselves as nonreligious. Yet there is evidence of a growing spiritual awakening in many sectors of society. Amidst Australia's economic prosperity and high levels of education are approximately 350,000 aborigines who speak about 20 aboriginal languages still needing Bible translation. **PRAY** that wealth and comfort will not numb Australians to their need for the Gospel. Pray for Bible translations in all aboriginal languages. Pray for those who read these new translations, that they would know the Living Word, Jesus Christ. *See John 1:14*

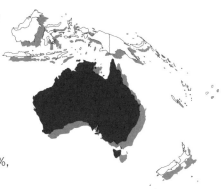

   Population: 20,264,082
   Capital: Canberra
   Language: English
   Literacy: 100%
   Income (GDP) per capita: $32,000
   Religions: Roman Catholic 26%, Anglican 21%,
      other Christian 21%, other or none 32%

AUSTRIA

While some Austrians know Christ in a personal relationship, the majority view Christianity as a cultural heritage to be maintained with traditional religious rituals. Evangelicals are a tiny minority who are frequently ostracized by family and friends because many Austrians have grown up believing that any church other than the Catholic Church is a cult. **PRAY** that Austrians would exchange the traditions of men for a personal relationship with Jesus Christ. Pray that Austrians who experience a personal relationship with Christ would not be bound by the fear of man, but would be bold in sharing their faith. *See Colossians 2:8–9*

   Population: 8,192,880
   Capital: Vienna
   Language: German
   Literacy: 98%
   Income (GDP) per capita: $32,900
   Religions: Roman Catholic 74%, none 12%,
      Protestant 5%, Islam 4%, other 5%

All the nations you have made will come and worship before you.
—PSALM 86:9

For [God] says to Moses, "I will have *Mercy* on whom I have mercy, and I will have compassion on whom I have compassion." It does not, therefore, depend on man's desire or effort, but on God's mercy.

—ROMANS 9:15–16

SUNDAY
Pray from Matthew 10:21–42

Prayer Concerns

Answers

MONDAY
Matthew 11

TUESDAY
Matthew 12:1–23

WEDNESDAY
Matthew 12:24–50

Prayer Concerns

Answers

THURSDAY
Matthew 13:1–30

FRIDAY
Matthew 13:31–58

SATURDAY
Matthew 14:1–21

Perhaps you do not know how to pray. Why don't you start now by saying, "God, be merciful to me, a sinner"? That simple, direct prayer, sincerely said, will open new horizons of spiritual victory for you and add a new dimension to your life.

—BILLY GRAHAM

"See, O *Lord*, how distressed I am! I am in
torment within, and in my heart I am disturbed. ..."
I say to myself, "The Lord is my portion; therefore
I will wait for him." The Lord is good to those whose
hope is in him, to the one who seeks him; it is good to
wait quietly for the salvation of the Lord.
—LAMENTATIONS 1:20; 3:24—26

SUNDAY
Pray from Matthew 14:22—36   *Prayer Concerns*   *Answers*

MONDAY
Matthew 15:1—20

TUESDAY
Matthew 15:21—39

WEDNESDAY
Matthew 16

Prayer Concerns   *Answers*

THURSDAY
Matthew 17

FRIDAY
Matthew 18:1–20

SATURDAY
Matthew 18:21–35

God even hears our prayers when we can't quite put them into words—times, for example, when our hearts are too burdened or confused even to speak. The Bible says, *"The Spirit helps us in our weakness. We do not know what we ought to pray for, but the Spirit himself intercedes for us with groans that words cannot express"* (Romans 8:26).

—BILLY GRAHAM

"Because he *Loves* me," says the Lord,
"I will rescue him; I will protect him, for he
acknowledges my name. He will call upon me,
and I will answer him."

—PSALM 91:14–15

SUNDAY
Pray from Matthew 19

Prayer Concerns   *Answers*

MONDAY
Matthew 20:1–16

TUESDAY
Matthew 20:17–34

WEDNESDAY
Matthew 21:1–22

Prayer Concerns   *Answers*

THURSDAY
Matthew 21:23–46

FRIDAY
Matthew 22:1–22

SATURDAY
Matthew 22:23–46

Prayer is simply talking to God—and the most important thing I can say about this is that God wants you to talk to Him!

—BILLY GRAHAM

Do not let this Book of the $\mathscr{Law}$ depart from your mouth; meditate on it day and night, so that you may be careful to do everything written in it. Then you will be prosperous and successful.

—JOSHUA 1:8

SUNDAY
Pray from Matthew 23:1–22

Prayer Concerns

Answers

MONDAY
Matthew 23:23–39

TUESDAY
Matthew 24:1–28

WEDNESDAY

Matthew 24:29–51

Prayer Concerns   *Answers*

THURSDAY

Matthew 25:1–30

FRIDAY

Matthew 25:31–46

SATURDAY

Matthew 26:1–25

Prayer and Bible study are inseparably linked. Effective prayer is born out of the prompting of God's Spirit as we read His Word.

—BILLY GRAHAM

Pray for Bangladesh

An overcrowded nation located on a vast, low-lying flood plain, Bangladesh is regularly subject to debilitating natural disasters. The site of intense poverty along with political and social unrest, it is an Islamic country with a tradition of allowing minority religions to exist quietly. The culture discourages conversion, only a tiny part of the population is Christian, and Islamic opposition has increased; even so, the Gospel message is going forward. **PRAY** for the safety and protection of those who are standing for Christ in Bangladesh. Pray for wisdom and courage for Bengali Christians to fearlessly proclaim the Gospel. *See Acts 4:29*

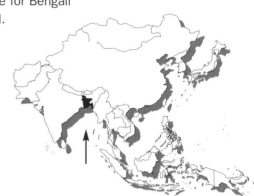

> Population: 147,365,352
> Capital: Dhaka
> Languages: Bangla, English
> Literacy: 43%
> Income (GDP) per capita: $2,100
> Religions: Islam 83%, Hindu 16%,
>   other 1%

Belarus

The people of Belarus, a former Soviet republic situated between Poland and Russia, struggle under the oppression of political dictatorship. Strict religious laws pose many problems for Christians. Despite persecution, the Church has responded with integrity and has continued to experience growth. Even as new believers regularly join evangelical Protestant churches, attendance at traditional Orthodox and Roman Catholic services has soared. **PRAY** that Belarus will experience political and spiritual freedom. Pray that Christians in Belarus will continue to respond with integrity, overcoming evil with good. *See Romans 12:21*

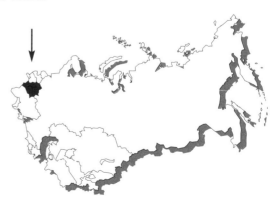

> Population: 10,293,011
> Capital: Minsk
> Languages: Belorussian, Russian
> Literacy: 100%
> Income (GDP) per capita: $7,700
> Religions: Eastern Orthodox 80%,
>   other 20%

BELGIUM

While Belgium's economic status is superb, its spiritual state is impoverished. Many Belgians call themselves Christian only because of family tradition. The evangelical church in Belgium makes up just over 1 percent of all Christians. One contributing factor is the relatively small number of Belgian and Flemish evangelical pastors and Christian workers. Despite this, Belgians who have experienced a personal relationship with Christ continue to grow in number. **PRAY** that the Lord will send revival to the people of Belgium. Pray that the Lord will raise up pastors and Christian leaders in Belgium to send out into His harvest fields. *See Matthew 9:37–38*

> Population: 10,379,067
> Capital: Brussels
> Languages: Dutch 60%, French 40%
> Literacy: 98%
> Income (GDP) per capita: $31,900
> Religions: Roman Catholic 75%,
>   other 25%

BENIN

Benin's rich historical heritage is rooted in the powerful Kingdom of Dahomey, which flourished in West Africa from the 1600s to the late 1800s. Roman Catholic missionaries introduced Christianity as early as 1680. Referred to as the home of voodoo, Benin is today considered the least evangelized non-Muslim country in Africa. The Church is steadily growing but faces a serious problem, because many who identify themselves as Christians continue to hold onto their voodoo practices. **PRAY** that Christians in Benin will turn wholly to the Lord, forsaking idolatry and false gods. *See 2 Corinthians 6:16–17*

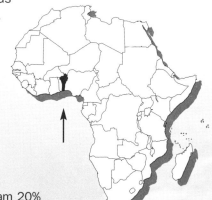

> Population: 7,862,944
> Capital: Porto-Novo
> Language: French
> Literacy: 41%
> Income (GDP) per capita: $1,100
> Religions: Indigenous 50%, Christian 30%, Islam 20%

All the nations you have made will come and worship before you.
—PSALM 86:9

As a young man, I *Wrote* to my mother, "I know that I know Jesus Christ, but I've lost my feeling. I can't seem to get anywhere in prayer. I don't feel anything." "Son, God is testing you," she wrote back. "He tells us to walk not by feeling but by faith, and when you don't feel anything, God may be closer to you than ever before. Through the darkness and through the fog, put your hand up by faith. You'll sense the touch of God."

—BILLY GRAHAM

Creative Prayer Suggestions

A key element in keeping prayer personal is making it creative. Often, routine is the assassin of effective prayer. Below are some ideas for creative prayer.

* Make a "prayer book" of pictures. This would work well for family, leaders, and missionaries. Often seeing people gives us a personal burden as we pray for them.

* Make a list of needy people in your church or neighborhood. Pray for them with your family, and explore ways that various family members can reach out to them.

* When praying for the nation and the world, pray about the front-page events of your local newspaper.

* Make a list of all the leaders in your church and their specific areas of ministry. Ask them for specific requests from time to time.

* As you use this journal and read the suggested Scriptures, keep notes of the needs and people who come to mind and pray for them. Then, think of ways you could help answer each prayer need. For instance, who among your acquaintances needs a *"cup of cold water"* (Matthew 10:42) from you today?

* Have your family find out more about some of the countries listed on the "Praying for the Nations" pages (beginning on page 23). Using sources such as *National Geographic*, do a pictorial display in a scrapbook or on a bulletin board and use that as a focal point for prayer.

* Get a list of all missionaries and organizations your church supports. Many have monthly newsletters that keep you informed so you can pray more specifically. Perhaps pray for one or two missionaries or organizations each month.

Now, our God, hear the *Prayers* and petitions
of your servant. ...We do not make requests of you
because we are righteous, but because of your
great mercy. O Lord, listen! O Lord, forgive! O Lord,
hear and act! For your sake, O my God, do not delay.

—DANIEL 9:17—19

SUNDAY
Pray from Matthew 26:26–50   *Prayer Concerns*   *Answers*

MONDAY
Matthew 26:51–75

TUESDAY
Matthew 27:1–26

WEDNESDAY
Matthew 27:27–50

Answers

THURSDAY
Matthew 27:51–66

FRIDAY
Matthew 28

SATURDAY
Mark 1:1–22

When you pray, pray! Too often we use petty little petitions, oratorical exercises, or the words of others rather than the cries of our inmost being.

—BILLY GRAHAM

Listen to my instruction and be *Wise*; do not
ignore it. Blessed is the man who listens to me,
watching daily at my doors.
— PROVERBS 8:33–34

SUNDAY
Pray from Mark 1:23–45

Prayer Concerns   *Answers*

MONDAY
Mark 2

TUESDAY
Mark 3:1–19

WEDNESDAY
Mark 3:20–35

Prayer Concerns

Answers

THURSDAY
Mark 4:1–20

FRIDAY
Mark 4:21–41

SATURDAY
Mark 5:1–20

The soul demands as much attention as the body. It needs fellowship and communion with God. It needs worship, quietness, and meditation. Unless the soul is fed and exercised daily, it becomes weak and shriveled, discontented, confused, restless.

—BILLY GRAHAM

If *You*, then, though you are evil, know how to
give good gifts to your children, how much more will
your Father in heaven give good gifts to those
who ask him!

—MATTHEW 7:11

SUNDAY
Mark 5:21–43

Prayer Concerns   *Answers*

MONDAY
Mark 6:1–29

TUESDAY
Mark 6:30–56

WEDNESDAY
Mark 7

Prayer Concerns   Answers

THURSDAY
Mark 8:1–21

FRIDAY
Mark 8:22–38

SATURDAY
Mark 9:1–29

So often we are inclined to think that the only answer God can give our prayers is "yes."
We need to remember that "no" is an answer also. ... God does not always give us what we
want; He gives us what we need. Just as a good parent does not grant all the requests of his
child, God does not answer every request in the way we desire.

                                                                —BILLY GRAHAM

Do not let your *Hands* hang limp. The
Lord your God is with you, he is mighty to save.
He will take great delight in you, he will quiet you with
his love, he will rejoice over you with singing.

—ZEPHANIAH 3:16—17

SUNDAY
Pray from Mark 9:30–50   *Prayer Concerns*   *Answers*

MONDAY
Mark 10:1–31

TUESDAY
Mark 10:32–52

WEDNESDAY
Mark 11:1–18

Prayer Concerns   *Answers*

THURSDAY
Mark 11:19–33

FRIDAY
Mark 12:1–27

SATURDAY
Mark 12:28–44

God wants us to talk with Him, our Heavenly Father, and He takes delight in us when we come to Him in prayer.

—BILLY GRAHAM

Pray for Bolivia

A beautiful, landlocked nation extending from the Andes Mountains to high-altitude plateaus to steamy eastern Amazon lowlands, Bolivia is one of the least developed and poorest nations in South America; about two-thirds of Bolivians live in poverty. Although nominally Catholic, half the population also follow indigenous Incan and Aymaran religious practices. Recently evangelical Christian churches have experienced significant growth. **PRAY** that God will ignite a passion for Jesus within the hearts of Christians living in poverty, that they may be rich in faith, and that the Church will continue to grow as people turn to Christ. *See James 2:5*

> Population: 8,989,046
> Capital: La Paz
> Languages: Spanish, Quechua, Aymara
> Literacy: 87%
> Income (GDP) per capita: $2,700
> Religions: Roman Catholic 95% (nominal),
>   Protestant 5%

Bosnia and Herzegovina

The Bosnian conflict of the 1990s caused a quarter million deaths and economic ruin, leaving impoverishment, deep scars, and an abiding hatred between ethnic groups who once lived together, spoke the same language, and even intermarried. Although evangelical churches are small and few, they have gained credibility for their willingness to bridge the ethnic divides. **PRAY** for revival within the Orthodox churches where a third of the population worship. Pray that the people of Bosnia and Herzegovina will experience the healing love of Christ that breaks down all hostility. Pray for evangelical churches to be leaders in peacemaking. *See Matthew 5:9*

> Population: 4,498,976
> Capital: Sarajevo
> Languages: Bosnian, Croatian, Serbian
> Literacy: N/A
> Income (GDP) per capita: $6,800
> Religions: Islam 40%, Orthodox 31%, Roman
>   Catholic 15%, other 14%

CANADA

Tolerance is a concept highly valued in Canadian society. While this is positive in many ways, it has made it difficult for many Canadians to consider Jesus' claim that He is the only way to the Father. An interesting trend in recent years is the number of Christians from Asia and Africa who immigrate to Canada for political or economic reasons. **PRAY** that Christian families settling in Canada will shine with the love of Jesus in an increasingly secular society. Pray that Canadians will not miss the Way, the Truth, and the Life. *See John 14:6*

   Population: 33,098,932
   Capital: Ottawa, Ontario
   Languages: English 59%, French 23%, Other 18%
   Literacy: 97%
   Income (GDP) per capita: $32,900
   Religions: Roman Catholic 43%, Protestant 23%,
      other 18%, none 16%

CHILE

This long, narrow country has one of the strongest economies in South America and nearly universal literacy. Chile has had a Christian presence since priests arrived in 1541. Chileans are overwhelmingly affiliated with Catholic or other churches, although many are Christian in name only. Pentecostal denominations have been active for a century; in recent years non-Pentecostal evangelical churches are growing significantly and many middle-class Chileans are seeking a more vital faith. **PRAY** for unity among Chile's many small church groups. Pray that many Chileans who claim Christianity as a religious affiliation will encounter Jesus Christ in a personal relationship. *See Matthew 7:21*

   Population: 16,134,219
   Capital: Santiago
   Language: Spanish
   Literacy: 96%
   Income (GDP) per capita: $11,300
   Religions: Roman Catholic 89%, Protestant 11%

All the nations you have made will come and worship before you.
—PSALM 86:9

I firmly believe *God* continues to answer
the prayers of His people even after He has
taken them to Heaven. Never forget that God isn't
bound by time the way we are. We see only the present
moment; God sees everything. We see only part of what
He is doing; He sees it all. Long after you and I are
gone, God will still be at work—and many of the things
we prayed for will finally come to pass.

—BILLY GRAHAM

A Powerful Way to Pray God's Word

BY ROBERT J. MORGAN

MANY YEARS AGO SEVERAL young college students sat around the old oak table in Ruth Bell Graham's kitchen, listening to her stories. We were lonely and homesick. College life had been rougher than expected. Ruth's eyes glowed as she told us of her own bouts with loneliness, particularly of an unsparing incident that once laid her low.

"When I was 13," she said, "my parents, missionaries in China, enrolled me in boarding school in what is now Pyongyang, North Korea. It was a difficult parting, and on my last night home, I earnestly prayed that I would die." Ruth didn't die, but arriving in Korea, she reeled under pounding waves of homesickness. Every night, she buried her head in her pillow and cried herself to sleep. Finally in desperation, she went to her sister, Rosa, also enrolled in Pyongyang.

"I don't know what to tell you to do," Rosa replied bluntly, "unless you take some verse and put your own name in it. See if that helps." Ruth picked up her Bible and turned to a favorite chapter, Isaiah 53, and put her name in it: "He was pierced for Ruth's transgressions, he was crushed for my iniquities; the punishment that brought Ruth peace was upon him, and by his wounds I am healed" (v. 5).

WHAT RUTH GRAHAM TAUGHT ME ABOUT PRAYER

"I claimed that verse and knew then," Ruth told us, "that I would make it."

CURE FOR A KNOTTED STOMACH

I have often remembered Mrs. Graham's words, and have developed a variation of that technique. For several years now, I've devoted a portion of my daily prayer time to taking various passages of Scripture and putting my name in them—or the names of others. I record these prayers in a journal as petitions to the Lord.

"God loves to be reminded of His promises," Ruth went on to tell us on that autumn evening in 1971. "He never rebukes us for asking too much."

GOD LOVES TO BE REMINDED OF HIS PROMISES.

Worriers like me must frequently remember that. We often suffer knotted stomachs, pounding heads, and spastic colons, when our real need is bent knees. James 5:16 teaches that the prayers of a righteous person are *"powerful and effective."* They can keep us and our loved ones from danger, spare us from evil, instill us with wisdom, and nudge us toward God.

But what exactly should we pray? Romans 8:26 warns that sometimes we *"do not know what we ought to pray for."* But when we pray using the words of Scripture, we can be confident of praying acceptably before God.

HE NEVER REBUKES US FOR ASKING TOO MUCH.

For example, I found a passage in Ephesians 4 that I adapted for my daughter Hannah. I wrote it in my prayer notebook, then offered it aloud to the Lord: Dear Lord, I pray today for Hannah, that you will help her avoid unwholesome talk, and teach her to speak only what is helpful in building others up according to their needs. Keep her from grieving your Holy Spirit.

Concerned for a struggling young friend, I prayed for him along the lines of Luke 11:1 and Hebrews 4:16—Heavenly Father, teach James to pray. May he learn to approach Your throne of grace with confidence so that he can receive mercy and find grace to help him in his time of need.

In praying for my missionary friend in the Ivory Coast of West Africa, I've leaned on Ephesians 6:19: God, I pray whenever Clint opens his mouth, words may be given him so that he will fearlessly make known the mystery of the Gospel.

And praying for my church, I have sometimes taken my cue from the Lord Jesus in John 17:23—Father, may we be brought to complete unity to let the world know that You sent us and have loved us.

HABITS WORTH FORMING

Keeping a prayer journal helps keep my habits on track, but those uncomfortable keeping a notebook can use the margins of their Bibles for the same purposes. As meaningful verses are found, they can be switched into prayers and offered aloud. A record of the person prayed for and the date can be jotted alongside the text with a fine-point pen.

Another version of this technique involves memorized Scripture. When retiring at night or while driving down the highway, reflect on a beloved verse and transform it into a prayer. Just the other day, after having said exactly the wrong thing to someone, I drove off while earnestly praying Psalm 141:3—*"Set a guard over my mouth, O Lord; keep watch over the door of my lips."*

This habit can also be extended to the hymnbook. Want to pray a special prayer for your mother? Adapt Frances Ridley Havergal's famous hymn to say: "Take Mom's life and let it be/Consecrated, Lord, to thee;/Take her moments and her days—/Let them flow in ceaseless praise." Instead of listening to the radio, use your drive time to pray for family and friends by singing your way down the highway, punching their names into the stanzas.

A Remarkable Prayer Time

Some time ago, my wife and I took in a troubled young man with a long history of drug and alcohol abuse. We loved him dearly and beamed at his progress. But after several months of sobriety, he suddenly relapsed into a vicious world of beer and cocaine.

The next six months were a nightmare, but he eventually consented to let us enroll him in a drug rehab program. He entered just before his birthday and I told him that in lieu of a present, I would pray for him for an hour when the day came.

When his birthday arrived, I wondered how I could pray so long for one person. Late in the evening after everyone else was in bed, I slipped to the living room and knelt by the sofa.

I opened my Bible to Genesis and thumbed through page after page. Before me were well-worn chapters, underlined verses, highlighted passages. One-by-one I adapted them into prayers for Mark.

> WHEN WE PRAY USING WORDS OF SCRIPTURE, WE CAN BE CONFIDENT OF PRAYING ACCEPTABLY BEFORE GOD.

I have seldom felt such power in prayer, and the hour went quickly. I ran out of time long before running out of verses. Meanwhile in the rehab center, Mark turned the corner. That was seven years ago, and he is still doing great. We can trace his turn-around to the very week of his birthday.

If you find your stomach knotting, your head pounding, and your teeth clenched, discover the simple remedy of bending your knees. Remember the advice that pulled Ruth Graham from depression. Find a portion of Scripture, and put a name in it.

O God, you are my God, earnestly I *Seek* you;
my soul thirsts for you, my body longs for you, in a dry
and weary land where there is no water.

—PSALM 63:1

SUNDAY
Pray from Mark 13:1–20

Prayer Concerns   *Answers*

MONDAY
Mark 13:21–37

TUESDAY
Mark 14:1–26

HOW TO PRAY FROM SCRIPTURE, SEE PAGE 49

WEDNESDAY
Mark 14:27–53

Prayer Concerns   *Answers*

THURSDAY
Mark 14:54–72

FRIDAY
Mark 15:1–25

SATURDAY
Mark 15:26–47

God says that only those who hunger and thirst after righteousness will receive it.
God thrusts this heavenly manna on no one. You must desire it above everything else.
Your yearning for God must supersede all other desires. It must be like a gnawing
hunger and a burning thirst.

—BILLY GRAHAM

Since *Praying* the day we heard about you, we have not stopped *Praying* for you and asking God to fill you with the knowledge of his will through all spiritual wisdom and understanding. And we pray this in order that you may live a life worthy of the Lord and may please him in every way: bearing fruit in every good work, growing in the knowledge of God.

—COLOSSIANS 1:9—10

SUNDAY
Pray from Mark 16

Prayer Concerns   *Answers*

MONDAY
Luke 1:1—20

TUESDAY
Luke 1:21—38

WEDNESDAY
Luke 1:39–56

Prayer Concerns   *Answers*

THURSDAY
Luke 1:57–80

FRIDAY
Luke 2:1–24

SATURDAY
Luke 2:25–52

It's easier to pray for someone we know rather than someone we don't know. But has it ever occurred to you that those you know the least may need your prayers the most? Don't let the fact that you don't know someone keep you from praying for them.

—BILLY GRAHAM

55

When your *Words* came, I ate them; they were
my joy and my heart's delight, for I bear your name,
O Lord God Almighty.

—JEREMIAH 15:16

SUNDAY
Pray from Luke 3

Prayer Concerns

Answers

MONDAY
Luke 4:1–30

TUESDAY
Luke 4:31–44

WEDNESDAY
Luke 5:1–16

Prayer Concerns

Answers

THURSDAY
Luke 5:17–39

FRIDAY
Luke 6:1–26

SATURDAY
Luke 6:27–49

Prayer by itself is like a diet without protein! Yes, prayer is important to our spiritual growth—but of even greater importance is God's Word, the Bible.

—BILLY GRAHAM

We do not know what we ought to pray for, but the Spirit himself intercedes for us with groans that words cannot express. And he who searches our hearts knows the mind of the Spirit, because the Spirit intercedes for the saints in accordance with God's will.

—ROMANS 8:26—27

SUNDAY
Pray from Luke 7:1–30

Prayer Concerns   *Answers*

MONDAY
Luke 7:31–50

TUESDAY
Luke 8:1–25

WEDNESDAY
Luke 8:26–56

Prayer Concerns   *Answers*

THURSDAY
Luke 9:1–17

FRIDAY
Luke 9:18–36

SATURDAY
Luke 9:37–62

Pray and ask God to guide you. ... Often, we try to tell God what we want Him to do—but ask Him to help you guard against this, and to seek His will instead of your own.

—BILLY GRAHAM

Pray for Colombia

Following Christ in one of the most violent countries on earth, Christians in Colombia face serious danger. Churches are forced to close, pastors are often kidnapped, and many Christians are killed for resisting the corrupting influence of the drug trade or simply because they live and worship amidst widespread lawlessness. Pervasive violence in a society, however, can open hearts to Christ. In recent years the Church has experienced explosive growth. **PRAY** for hundreds of thousands of new believers to remain strong in their faith. Pray that Christians will have the courage to love and pray for those who harm them.
See Matthew 5:44

Population: 43,593,035
Capital: Bogotá
Language: Spanish
Literacy: 93%
Income (GDP) per capita: $7,100
Religions: Roman Catholic 90%, other 10%

Costa Rica

Some churches in Costa Rica have become "sending churches," doubling the number of Christian missionaries sent out to other countries over the past decade. At the same time, large numbers of Costa Ricans consider their religious affiliation to be a matter of form and tradition, not understanding they can have a personal relationship with Christ. **PRAY** that God will open the hearts of Costa Ricans to the free gift of grace through faith. Thank God that Costa Rican churches have become active partners in His heart for the nations, and pray for fruit from this missionary effort. *See Romans 10:14–15*

Population: 4,075,261
Capital: San José
Languages: Spanish, English
Literacy: 96%
Income (GDP) per capita: $10,100
Religions: Roman Catholic 76%,
    evangelical 14%, other 7%, none 3%

ECUADOR

Formerly a country of great resistance to the Gospel, Ecuador was where Jim Elliot and four others were martyred decades ago. Today, believers in Ecuador are multiplying rapidly. A few years ago, the Billy Graham Evangelistic Association partnered with 3,100 local churches in a nationwide outreach called *Mi Esperanza*, during which church members across the country invited friends and neighbors into their homes to watch TV broadcasts prepared by BGEA especially for Ecuador. Churches later identified 85,000 people who made commitments. **PRAY** that the thousands who have recently made decisions for Christ will continue to abide in Him. *See John 15:4*

> Population: 13,547,510
> Capital: Quito
> Language: Spanish
> Literacy: 93%
> Income (GDP) per capita: $3,900
> Religions: Roman Catholic 95%, other 5%

EL SALVADOR

Violence against children is recognized as a severe and surprisingly widespread problem in El Salvador. Some of this is because of family instability caused when so many mothers come to the United States to work, leaving children with relatives. Many angry children join gangs and resort to crime. **PRAY** for strong, enforced legislation that will prevent child abuse. Pray for an economic solution that would keep mothers with families. Pray that Christ will heal the wounded children, give them grace to forgive, and raise them up as loving parents who will break abusive family cycles. *See Mark 10:16*

> Population: 6,822,378
> Capital: San Salvador
> Languages: Spanish, Nahua
> Literacy: 80%
> Income (GDP) per capita: $5,100
> Religions: Catholic 83%, other 17%

All the nations you have made will come and worship before you.

—PSALM 86:9

Three times a day [Daniel] got down on
his knees and prayed, giving thanks to his God,
just as he had done before.

—DANIEL 6:10

SUNDAY
Pray from Luke 10:1–24

Prayer Concerns   *Answers*

MONDAY
Luke 10:25–42

TUESDAY
Luke 11:1–28

WEDNESDAY
Luke 11:29–54

Prayer Concerns

Answers

THURSDAY
Luke 12:1–31

FRIDAY
Luke 12:32–59

SATURDAY
Luke 13:1–22

The three most important things you can do are, number one, pray ... number two, pray ... number three, pray.

—BILLY GRAHAM

And my God will meet *All* your needs according
to his glorious riches in Christ Jesus.

—PHILIPPIANS 4:19

SUNDAY
Pray from Luke 13:23–35

Prayer Concerns

Answers

MONDAY
Luke 14:1–24

TUESDAY
Luke 14:25–35

WEDNESDAY
Luke 15:1–10

THURSDAY
Luke 15:11–32

FRIDAY
Luke 16

SATURDAY
Luke 17:1–19

God not only cares about our needs but He is also delighted when we bring them to Him in prayer. Jesus said, "*If you ... know how to give good gifts to your children, how much more will your Father in heaven give good gifts to those who ask him!*" (see Matthew 7:11).

—BILLY GRAHAM

I know what it is to be in *Need*, and I know what it is to have plenty. I have learned the secret of being content in any and every situation, whether well fed or hungry, whether living in plenty or in want.

—PHILIPPIANS 4:12

SUNDAY
Pray from Luke 17:20–37

Prayer Concerns

Answers

MONDAY
Luke 18:1–23

TUESDAY
Luke 18:24–43

WEDNESDAY
Luke 19:1–27

THURSDAY
Luke 19:28–48

FRIDAY
Luke 20:1–26

SATURDAY
Luke 20:27–47

Remember: There is a difference between our needs and our wants. We may want something for ourselves but it might not be something we really need. When we honestly need something (and don't simply want it), God tells us to bring it to Him and trust Him for the outcome.

—BILLY GRAHAM

And [Moses] said, "Please, *Show* me Your glory." ...
Now the Lord descended in the cloud and stood with him
there, and proclaimed the name of the Lord.
And the Lord passed before him and proclaimed,
"The Lord, the Lord God, merciful and gracious,
longsuffering, and abounding in goodness and truth ... ."
—EXODUS 33:18; 34:5—6 (NKJV)

SUNDAY
Pray from Luke 21:1—19

Prayer Concerns   *Answers*

MONDAY
Luke 21:20—38

TUESDAY
Luke 22:1—20

WEDNESDAY
Luke 22:21–46

Prayer Concerns

Answers

THURSDAY
Luke 22:47–71

FRIDAY
Luke 23:1–25

SATURDAY
Luke 23:26–56

How can you keep your mind from wandering when you pray? Remember what you are doing: talking to God. If you had an opportunity to talk with the president, I doubt if your mind would wander. But you and I have the privilege of talking to someone far greater: the King of kings and the Lord of lords!

—BILLY GRAHAM

Pray for Estonia

Decades ago, Estonian churches experienced a spiritual awakening that impacted the entire land. During the years of Soviet domination and oppression, that fire dwindled so that today more than two-thirds of Estonians identify with no religion. Many Estonians still harbor a deep resentment toward ethnic Russians. Several churches in Estonia invited Franklin Graham and the Billy Graham Evangelistic Association to join them in a major evangelistic outreach during 2009. **PRAY** that Christians in Estonia would demonstrate the love of Christ by overcoming animosity toward Russian neighbors. Pray that God will restore and revive the body of Christ in Estonia. *See Psalm 85:6*

> Population: 1,324,333
> Capital: Tallinn
> Languages: Estonian, Russian
> Literacy: 100%
> Income (GDP) per capita: $16,400
> Religions: Unaffiliated or unspecified 66%,
>   Lutheran 14%, Orthodox 13%, none 6%,
>   other 1%

France

France today has one of the highest populations of Muslims in Europe—approximately 5.5 million. Once a largely Christian nation, the majority of people in France are now considered to be unreached by the Gospel. Many with a nominal Catholic affiliation are apathetic or oblivious about matters of faith, Protestant churches are few, and church-planting efforts struggle to bear fruit. **PRAY** that those who have not heard the Gospel in France will be reached with the Good News of Jesus Christ. Pray that this nation with a rich Christian heritage will experience spiritual restoration. *See Psalm 80:19*

> Population: 60,876,136
> Capital: Paris
> Language: French
> Literacy: 99%
> Income (GDP) per capita: $30,000
> Religions: Roman Catholic 86%, Islam 8%,
>   Protestant 2%, other 4%

THE GAMBIA

The West African nation of The Gambia is a narrow strip of land almost completely surrounded by Senegal. Christian churches are established mostly in the coastal area. The Fulani and Wolof peoples are inland groups who practice Islam but have a tradition of openness to discussing other religions. Christian evangelism is not generally opposed, but relatively few Fulani or Wolof people have moved beyond talk to follow Christ. **PRAY** for effective strategies to introduce Christ to these large ethnic groups. Pray for Bible translations in all Gambian languages. Pray for supportive Christian communities for all new believers. *See Acts 19:21–22*

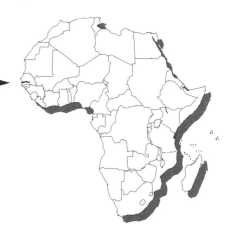

> Population: 1,641,564
> Capital: Banjul
> Languages: English, Mandinka, Wolof, Fula
> Literacy: 40%
> Income (GDP) per capita: $1,800
> Religions: Islam 90%, Christian 9%, other 1%

GEORGIA

Georgia became a Christian nation in the fourth century. The Georgian Orthodox Church proved to be a key factor in preserving a national identity through the turmoil of the next 1,700 years. Georgia was ruled by Russia from 1801 until the Soviet breakup in 1991. Joseph Stalin, himself a Georgian, helped strip the church of its role in society. Today there is hope of renewal in the ancient Orthodox church, and Protestant churches are growing, especially in poor communities. **PRAY** that the Lord will restore His Spirit to the Georgian Orthodox church and provide leadership for growing Protestant churches. *See Psalm 107:14*

> Population: 4,661,473
> Capital: Tbilisi
> Languages: Georgian, Russian
> Literacy: 99%
> Income (GDP) per capita: $3,300
> Religions: Orthodox 84%, Islam 10%, other 6%

All the nations you have made will come and worship before you.
—PSALM 86:9

"Lord, I have heard of your fame; I stand in awe
of your deeds, O Lord. Renew them in our day, in
our time make them known; in wrath remember mercy."

God came. … His glory covered the heavens
and his praise filled the earth.

—HABAKKUK 3:2—3

SUNDAY
Pray from Luke 24:1—35

Prayer Concerns

Answers

MONDAY
Luke 24:36—53

TUESDAY
John 1:1—28

WEDNESDAY
John 1:29–51

THURSDAY
John 2

FRIDAY
John 3:1–18

SATURDAY
John 3:19–36

Who knows what God might do if His people began to pray fervently for spiritual revival? Perhaps one reason Satan has gained such a hold on so many lives is because we don't pray enough. Our prayer should be that of the Prophet Habakkuk: "I stand in awe of your deeds, O Lord. Renew them in our day, in our time make them known" (see Habakkuk 3:2).

—BILLY GRAHAM

I pray also that the *Eyes* of your heart may be
enlightened in order / that you may know the hope
to which he has called / you, the riches of his glorious
inheritance in the saints, and his incomparably great
power for us who believe. That power is like the working
of his mighty strength, which he exerted in Christ
when he raised him from the dead.

—EPHESIANS 1:18–20

SUNDAY
Pray from John 4:1–30

Prayer Concerns

Answers

MONDAY
John 4:31–54

TUESDAY
John 5:1–24

WEDNESDAY
John 5:25–47

Prayer Concerns

Answers

THURSDAY
John 6:1–21

FRIDAY
John 6:22–44

SATURDAY
John 6:45–71

The Bible says God "*is able to do immeasurably more than all we ask or imagine, according to his power that is at work within us*" (see Ephesians 3:20). One of the ways His power is at work in us is through the prayers of His people, and that's one reason why we should always pray when we face hard times.

—BILLY GRAHAM

Therefore, as God's *Chosen* people, holy and
dearly loved, clothe yourselves with compassion,
kindness, humility, gentleness and patience. Bear with
each other and forgive whatever grievances you may have
against one another. Forgive as the Lord forgave you.

—COLOSSIANS 3:12–13

SUNDAY
Pray from John 7:1–27

Prayer Concerns   *Answers*

MONDAY
John 7:28–53

TUESDAY
John 8:1–27

INSERT A NAME INTO COLOSSIANS 3:12–15 FOR PRAYER

WEDNESDAY
John 8:28–59

Prayer Concerns

Answers

THURSDAY
John 9:1–23

FRIDAY
John 9:24–41

SATURDAY
John 10:1–23

The most eloquent prayer is the prayer through hands that heal and bless.

—BILLY GRAHAM

This is what the Lord says, ... "*Call* to me
and I will answer you and tell you great and unsearchable
things you do not know."
—JEREMIAH 33:2—3

SUNDAY
Pray from John 10:24–42

Prayer Concerns   *Answers*

MONDAY
John 11:1–29

TUESDAY
John 11:30–57

ASK IN PRAYER FOR NEW INSIGHTS AND FRESH KNOWLEDGE

WEDNESDAY
John 12:1–26

Prayer Concerns

Answers

THURSDAY
John 12:27–50

FRIDAY
John 13:1–20

SATURDAY
John 13:21–38

A mystery and wonder of prayer is that God often waits until someone asks. I once heard it said that Heaven's storeroom is full of answers for which no one bothered to ask.

—BILLY GRAHAM

Pray for Ghana

In 1957, Ghana became the first black African colony of Great Britain to gain independence, setting a pattern for the continent. Ghana has freedom of religion, and Ghanaians are receptive to the Gospel. Current economic difficulties, including unemployment and poverty, have created great stress. The youth are especially weary with the current conditions and spiritually open. **PRAY** that the Lord will enable churches to effectively disciple new converts, who are often tempted to continue dabbling in animistic, occult, or materialistic practices. Pray for the weary youth of Ghana, that they would find their hope and strength in Jesus Christ. *See Isaiah 40:30–31*

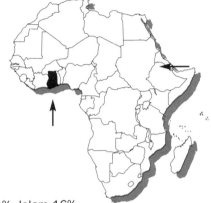

> Population: 22,409,572
> Capital: Accra
> Languages: English, African languages
> Literacy: 75%
> Income (GDP) per capita: $2,400
> Religions: Christian 63%, Indigenous beliefs 21%, Islam 16%

Greece

Nearly all Greeks identify themselves as Orthodox Christians. The Greek Orthodox Church embraces the idea that involvement with any other church is an affront to Greek culture and identity; as a result, many Greeks perceive Christianity as primarily a cultural tradition rather than a life commitment. **PRAY** that Greeks will see through their cultural religion and discover abundant life in knowing Christ personally. Pray that God will send a fresh awakening to the Greek Orthodox Church and raise up bold witnesses among the nation's own people who will exemplify lives given over completely to Christ. *See Titus 3:5–6*

> Population: 10,688,058
> Capital: Athens
> Language: Greek
> Literacy: 98%
> Income (GDP) per capita: $22,800
> Religions: Greek Orthodox 98%, other 2%

Haiti

Haiti is the least developed country in the Western Hemisphere and one of the poorest countries in the world. Christians have a great opportunity to minister the love of Jesus Christ through acts of mercy and love in this impoverished country. Much of the country intermixes the practice of Voodoo with some form or appearance of Christianity. **PRAY** that Haitians will forsake idolatry. Pray for committed Christians from Haiti and other nations to continue to pour out the tender mercies of the Lord so that God's light may shine on those living in darkness. *See Luke 1:78–79*

   Population: 8,308,504

   Capital: Port-au-Prince

   Languages: Creole and French

   Literacy: 53%

   Income (GDP) per capita: $1,600

   Religions: Roman Catholic 80%, Protestant 16%, other 4%;
      approximately 50% also practice Voodoo

Honduras

Natural disasters, including hurricanes and droughts, are common in Honduras and greatly damage the country's economy. Thus, the people of Honduras have one of the lowest average incomes in the Western Hemisphere. Hondurans comprise 60 percent of those with HIV in Central America. In the midst of these challenges, the church is experiencing substantial growth. **PRAY** that new believers will be discipled by caring churches. Pray that God will give the country's leaders wisdom in countering the growing problem with HIV. Pray that the Lord will sustain the poor in Honduras and make Himself known to them. *See Psalm 72:12*

   Population: 7,326,496

   Capital: Tegucigalpa

   Language: Spanish

   Literacy: 76%

   Income (GDP) per capita: $2,800

   Religions: Roman Catholic 97%, Protestant 3%

All the nations you have made will come and worship before you.

—Psalm 86:9

Consider it pure *Joy*, my brothers, whenever you face trials of many kinds, because you know that the testing of your faith develops perseverance. Perseverance must finish its work so that you may be mature and complete, not lacking anything.

—JAMES 1:2–4

SUNDAY
Pray from John 14

Prayer Concerns

Answers

MONDAY
John 15

TUESDAY
John 16

WEDNESDAY
John 17

THURSDAY
John 18:1–18

FRIDAY
John 18:19–40

SATURDAY
John 19:1–22

All the masterpieces of art contain both light and shadow. A happy life is not one filled with only sunshine, but one which uses both light and shadow to produce beauty.

—BILLY GRAHAM

If you remain in *Me* and my words remain in
you, ask whatever you wish, and it will be given you.
This is to my Father's glory, that you bear much fruit,
showing yourselves to be my disciples.

—JOHN 15:7—8

SUNDAY
Pray from John 19:23–42   *Prayer Concerns*   *Answers*

MONDAY
John 20

TUESDAY
John 21

WEDNESDAY
Acts 1

Prayer Concerns   *Answers*

THURSDAY
Acts 2:1–21

FRIDAY
Acts 2:22–47

SATURDAY
Acts 3

Prayer is not our using of God; it more often puts us in a position where God can use us.

—BILLY GRAHAM

Never be lacking in *Zeal*, but keep your spiritual
fervor, serving the Lord. Be joyful in hope,
patient in affliction, faithful in prayer.

—ROMANS 12:11—12

SUNDAY
Pray from Acts 4:1–22

Prayer Concerns   *Answers*

MONDAY
Acts 4:23–37

TUESDAY
Acts 5:1–21

WEDNESDAY
Acts 5:22–42

Prayer Concerns

Answers

THURSDAY
Acts 6

FRIDAY
Acts 7:1–21

SATURDAY
Acts 7:22–43

We are to pray in times of adversity, lest we become faithless and unbelieving. We are to pray in times of prosperity, lest we become boastful and proud. We are to pray in times of danger, lest we become fearful and doubting. We need to pray in times of security, lest we become self-sufficient.

—BILLY GRAHAM

I pray that out of *His* glorious riches he may
strengthen you with power through his Spirit in your
inner being, so that Christ may dwell in your hearts
through faith. And I pray that you, being rooted and
established in love, may have power.

—EPHESIANS 3:16—18

SUNDAY
Pray from Acts 7:44–60

Prayer Concerns   *Answers*

MONDAY
Acts 8:1–25

TUESDAY
Acts 8:26–40

WEDNESDAY
Acts 9:1–21

Prayer Concerns   *Answers*

THURSDAY
Acts 9:22–43

FRIDAY
Acts 10:1–23

SATURDAY
Acts 10:24–48

You cannot afford to be too busy to pray. A prayerless Christian is a powerless Christian.

—BILLY GRAHAM

PRAY FOR INDIA

India is a nation of over 1 billion people. Although 94 percent of the people are either Hindu or Muslim, there are millions of Christians. A few years ago, the Billy Graham Evangelistic Association partnered with 80,000 local churches throughout India in an evangelistic strategy called *My Hope*. The churches recruited more than a million Christian households to invite non-Christian friends and neighbors into their homes to watch special TV broadcasts prepared by BGEA especially for India.

To date, churches in India have documented well more than 4.5 million individuals who made decisions for Christ. **PRAY** for this vast host of new believers and for the churches discipling them. *See Acts 16:5*

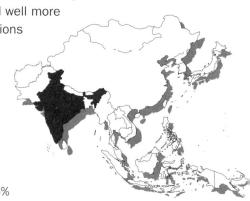

    Population: 1,095,351,995
    Capital: New Delhi
    Languages: Hindi, English
    Literacy: 60%
    Income (GDP) per capita: $3,400
    Religions: Hindu 81%, Islam 13%, other 6%

IRAN

Iran has been home to Christian churches since the fourth century. After the 1979 takeover by the Shiite Islamic government, life became so difficult for non-Muslims that most churches began steadily shrinking due to emigration. Although Christians make up only a tiny minority and conversion to Christianity is prohibited by religious law, some churches are nonetheless growing, especially Iranian Assemblies of God and Anglican churches, along with some smaller, independent churches. Some churches have gone underground to survive.

PRAY that God will grant continued courage to churches under pressure and strengthen the faith of Christians under persecution in Iran. *See Acts 4:29*

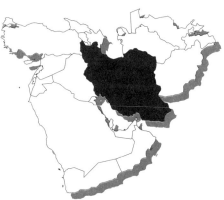

    Population: 68,688,433
    Capital: Tehran
    Languages: Farsi (Persian), Turkic, Kurdish
    Literacy: 79%
    Income (GDP) per capita: $8,100
    Religions: Islam 98% (Shi'a 89%, Sunni 9%),
      other 2%

IRAQ

Christians have lived in Iraq for 2,000 years, and some churches today still worship in Aramaic, the language Jesus spoke. Persecution escalated during the upheavals that have plagued Iraq since the 2003 overthrow of the nation's dictator, forcing about one-fourth of all Christian families to flee into exile. Those who remain are regularly harassed, and some are being killed. **PRAY** for peace and stability in the land the Bible calls Babylon. Pray that churches will maintain a clear witness and that Iraqi people will see the Gospel as an invitation from the living God and not a political persuasion associated with the West. *See Daniel 4:34*

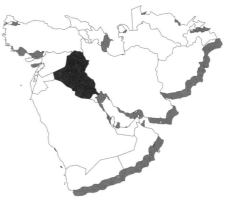

>   Population: 26,783,383
>   Capital: Baghdad
>   Languages: Arabic, Kurdish
>   Literacy: 40%
>   Income (GDP) per capita: $3,400
>   Religions: Islam 97% (Shiite 63%, Sunni 34%), other 3%

ISRAEL

Most Israeli citizens are Jewish, although a substantial minority are Arabs. Since 1948, at least 2.5 million Jews have resettled from other parts of the world. Israel is the only nation where Judaism is the dominant religion. **PRAY** for Israelis who are Christians, including Jews who are often ostracized by their society for accepting Jesus as Messiah. Pray for Arab Christians in and around Israel who are marginalized by both Jews and other Arabs. Pray for respite from violence and the threat of violence in Israel and surrounding nations. *See Isaiah 45:17*

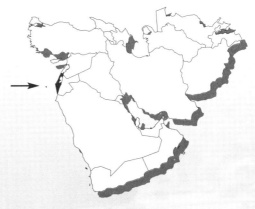

>   Population: 6,352,117
>   Capital: Jerusalem
>   Languages: Hebrew, Arabic, English
>   Literacy: 95%
>   Income (GDP) per capita: $22,300
>   Religions: Judaism 77%, Islam 16%,
>   Christian 2%, other 5%

All the nations you have made will come and worship before you.
—PSALM 86:9

Jesus said to them, "My Father is *Always* at his work to this very day, and I, too, am working."
—JOHN 5:17

SUNDAY
Pray from Acts 11

Prayer Concerns   *Answers*

MONDAY
Acts 12

TUESDAY
Acts 13:1–25

WEDNESDAY
Acts 13:26–52

Prayer Concerns   *Answers*

THURSDAY
Acts 14

FRIDAY
Acts 15:1–21

SATURDAY
Acts 15:22–41

When we think of "unanswered" prayer, it may be that we do not understand the way in which God responds to our requests. ... Sometimes our prayers are answered in a way that we fail to recognize. ... If your prayers are not always answered as you expect, it is not because God is not working in the situation.

—BILLY GRAHAM

I call on you, O God, for you *Will* answer me;
give ear to me and hear my prayer. Show the wonder of
your great love, you who save by your right hand those
who take refuge in you from their foes. Keep me as the
apple of your eye; hide me in the shadow of your wings.

—PSALM 17:6—8

SUNDAY
Pray from Acts 16:1–21

Prayer Concerns

Answers

MONDAY
Acts 16:22–40

TUESDAY
Acts 17:1–15

CREATIVE WAYS TO ENLIVEN YOUR PRAYER TIME, SEE PAGE 37

WEDNESDAY
Acts 17:16–34

Prayer Concerns

Answers

THURSDAY
Acts 18

FRIDAY
Acts 19:1–20

SATURDAY
Acts 19:21–41

My time spent in prayer with You, dear Lord, is the highlight of my day. To know You are waiting to have this communion humbles me. Yet You say I can come boldly—this I do now, knowing You hear me!

—BILLY GRAHAM

I cried out to him with my *Mouth*; his praise
was on my tongue. If I had cherished sin in my heart,
the Lord would not have listened; but God has surely
listened and heard my voice in prayer. Praise be to God,
who has not rejected my prayer or withheld his love from me!

—PSALM 66:17—20

SUNDAY
Pray from Acts 20:1—16

Prayer Concerns

Answers

MONDAY
Acts 20:17—38

TUESDAY
Acts 21:1—17

HOW TO TALK FREELY WITH GOD, SEE PAGE 4

WEDNESDAY
Acts 21:18–40

Prayer Concerns　　　　　　　　　　　　*Answers*

THURSDAY
Acts 22

FRIDAY
Acts 23:1–15

SATURDAY
Acts 23:16–35

Let me pour everything out to You, Lord. Thank You for the knowledge that You hear me!

—BILLY GRAHAM

I pray that you, being *Rooted* and established in love, may have power, together with all the saints, to grasp how wide and long and high and deep is the love of Christ, and to know this love that surpasses knowledge—that you may be filled to the measure of all the fullness of God.

—EPHESIANS 3:17—19

SUNDAY
Pray from Acts 24

Prayer Concerns

Answers

MONDAY
Acts 25

TUESDAY
Acts 26

WEDNESDAY
Acts 27:1–26

Prayer Concerns   *Answers*

THURSDAY
Acts 27:27–44

FRIDAY
Acts 28

SATURDAY
Romans 1

Jesus considered prayer more important than food, for the Bible says that hours before breakfast, "In the morning, rising up a great while before day, he went out, and departed into a solitary place, and there prayed" (see Mark 1:35).

—BILLY GRAHAM

Pray for Japan

The intense work ethic and strong Buddhist roots in Japan have blinded most from receiving the Good News of Jesus Christ. Less than 1 percent of Japanese people are Christians, and the average Japanese church has an attendance of 20 to 30 with very few men. Recently, evangelistic meetings have flourished among Japanese businessmen, giving many an outlet for fellowship and others an opportunity to hear the Gospel. **PRAY** that God will open the eyes of many in Japan caught in cultural norms that blind them to the Gospel. Pray that evangelistic business meetings will raise up leaders for Christ in Japan. *See Ephesians 1:17–18*

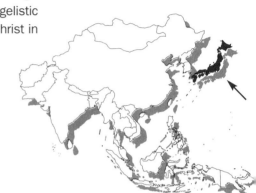

> Population: 127,463,611
> Capital: Tokyo
> Language: Japanese
> Literacy: 99%
> Income (GDP) per capita: $30,700
> Religions: Shintoist and Buddhist 84%,
> other 16%

Mexico

The church in Mexico is in a period of significant fruitfulness. A growing number of Roman Catholics are embracing the message of salvation by grace alone. A few years ago, 20,290 local churches partnered with the Billy Graham Evangelistic Association in a nationwide outreach strategy carried out by Christian families in their own neighborhoods. In the weeks and months that followed, participants and churches documented 397,424 people who made decisions for Christ. **PRAY** that Mexicans will continue to experience the freedom that comes through embracing salvation by grace. Pray for the many new believers and the churches discipling them. *See Ephesians 2:8–10*

> Population: 107,449,525
> Capital: Mexico City
> Language: Spanish
> Literacy: 92%
> Income (GDP) per capita: $10,100
> Religions: Roman Catholic 89%,
> Protestant 6%, other 5%

Moldova

Sandwiched between Ukraine and Romania, Moldova is a small, densely populated nation with a mixture of ethnic Moldovans, Russians, Ukrainians, Bulgarians, and Gagauz (a Turkic group). Most citizens are nominally Orthodox. Although few attend church and many have never heard the Gospel, the people as a whole are spiritually open. When Franklin Graham led evangelistic meetings recently, 93,000 people came by train, by bus, and on foot from throughout Moldova and thousands made decisions for Christ. Despite some opposition, churches are growing. **PRAY** for evangelical churches to continue to minister with boldness and compassion. Pray for awakening in the Orthodox Christian church. *See Jeremiah 29:13*

Population: 4,466,706

Capital: Chisinau

Languages: Moldovan, Russian

Literacy: 99%

Income (GDP) per capita: $2,100

Religions: Eastern Orthodox 98%,
Jewish 1.5%, other 0.5%

Mongolia

In the past 17 years, the number of Christians in Mongolia has skyrocketed from a handful to 20,000. The increase has stirred opposition, with Buddhist leaders pressing the idea that Christianity is inconsistent with Mongolia's national identity as a fiercely independent people rooted in the Mongol dynasty of Genghis Khan. The recent growth and multiplication of churches has created a dire need for trained pastors, teachers, and other Christian leadership, including those gifted to reach youth. **PRAY** that the Lord will raise up passionate, equipped shepherds, leaders, evangelists, and youth workers within the Mongolian Church. *See Jeremiah 3:15*

Population: 2,832,224

Capital: Ulaanbaatar

Languages: Mongolian, Turkic, and Russian

Literacy: 99%

Income (GDP) per capita: $2,200

Religions: Buddhist Lamaist 50%, none 40%, Islam 4%, other 6%

All the nations you have made will come and worship before you.

—PSALM 86:9

I lift up my eyes to *You*, to you whose throne is in heaven. As the eyes of slaves look to the hand of their master, as the eyes of a maid look to the hand of her mistress, so our eyes look to the Lord our God, till he shows us his mercy.

—PSALM 123:1—2

SUNDAY
Pray from Romans 2

Prayer Concerns

Answers

MONDAY
Romans 3

TUESDAY
Romans 4

WEDNESDAY
Romans 5

Prayer Concerns

Answers

THURSDAY
Romans 6

FRIDAY
Romans 7

SATURDAY
Romans 8:1–21

The reason many of the great saints have closed their eyes while praying is to shut out the affairs of the world so that their minds could be completely concentrated on their conversations with God. However, nowhere in Scripture does it say that even the closing of the eyes is important.

—BILLY GRAHAM

For as many as are *Led* by the Spirit of God, these are sons of God. For you did not receive the spirit of bondage again to fear, but you received the Spirit of adoption by whom we cry out, "Abba, Father." The Spirit Himself bears witness with our spirit that we are children of God.

—ROMANS 8:14–16 (NKJV)

SUNDAY
Pray from Romans 8:22–39

Prayer Concerns   *Answers*

MONDAY
Romans 9:1–15

TUESDAY
Romans 9:16–33

WEDNESDAY
Romans 10

Prayer Concerns   *Answers*

THURSDAY
Romans 11:1–18

FRIDAY
Romans 11:19–36

SATURDAY
Romans 12

Jesus said, "When ye pray, say, Our Father..." (see Matthew 6:9). This is a great comfort because God has a particular responsibility to His children.

—BILLY GRAHAM

Why do you call me, "Lord, Lord," and do not do what I say?

—LUKE 6:46

SUNDAY
Pray from Romans 13

Prayer Concerns

Answers

MONDAY
Romans 14

TUESDAY
Romans 15:1–13

WEDNESDAY
Romans 15:14–33

Prayer Concerns

Answers

THURSDAY
Romans 16

FRIDAY
1 Corinthians 1

SATURDAY
1 Corinthians 2

Dynamic prayer emanates from an obedient heart.

—BILLY GRAHAM

You did not choose me, but I *Chose* you and
appointed you to go and bear fruit—fruit that will last.
Then the Father will give you whatever you ask in my name.

—JOHN 15:16

SUNDAY
Pray from I Corinthians 3

Prayer Concerns

Answers

MONDAY
I Corinthians 4

TUESDAY
I Corinthians 5

WEDNESDAY
1 Corinthians 6

Prayer Concerns   *Answers*

_____   _____

_____   _____

_____   _____

_____   _____

THURSDAY
1 Corinthians 7:1–19

_____   _____

_____   _____

_____   _____

_____   _____

FRIDAY
1 Corinthians 7:20–40

_____   _____

_____   _____

_____   _____

_____   _____

SATURDAY
1 Corinthians 8

_____   _____

_____   _____

_____   _____

_____   _____

Every religion teaches that people ought to pray, but only the Christian faith promises that God will answer.

—BILLY GRAHAM

PRAY FOR MYANMAR

Formerly called Burma, Myanmar is ruled by a military government that enforces strict control of society, including religious activities. When a massive cyclone devastated Myanmar's delta region in 2008, causing extensive suffering, the government blocked most offers of aid. The few officially sanctioned churches are restricted by law to speaking of Jesus only within their building. Underground churches face severe risks but are growing. **PRAY** that Christians in Myanmar will be granted freedom to gather for worship and fellowship with each other. Pray for courage among Christians under persecution. Pray for basic human freedom for all citizens of Myanmar. *See Psalm 119:130*

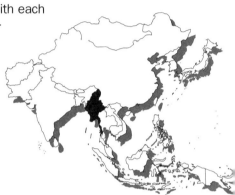

Population: 47,382,633

Capital: Rangoon

Language: Burmese

Literacy: 83%

Income (GDP) per capita: $1,600

Religions: Buddhist 89%, Christian 4%,
 Islam 4%, other 3%

NETHERLANDS

Prostitution is open and legal in the Netherlands. Many desperate women resort to this trade because of drug addictions or poverty. Others are seeking to escape impoverishment or oppression in third world countries, subjecting themselves to danger and degradation in Europe. Many Dutch citizens, 40 percent of whom claim no religion, are indifferent to the corrupting impact of the sex trade. **PRAY** for the relatively few Christians who undertake the difficult ministry of reaching out to those in the prostitution industry. Pray that women will see their worth in God's eyes. Pray that the Gospel will be heard in an apathetic society. *See Jeremiah 29:11–12*

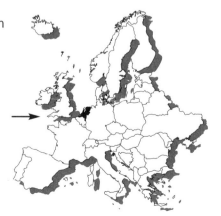

Population: 16,491,461

Capital: Amsterdam

Languages: Dutch, Frisian

Literacy: 99%

Income (GDP) per capita: $30,600

Religions: None 41%, Roman Catholic 31%,
 Dutch Reformed 13%, Calvinist 7%,
 Islam 6%, other 2%

Nicaragua

As a result of years of civil strife and political upheaval, along with economic devastation brought on by government policies and natural disasters, hopelessness pervades many segments of Nicaraguan society. Children are especially hurting, due to the increasing rarity of two-parent families. Churches within the country have suffered a great deal of division. In spite of all this, Nicaraguan churches are growing, Bible schools are flourishing, and Christians are engaged in strong, Christ-centered evangelism. **PRAY** for a change in economic conditions and cultural attitudes that would result in more stable families. Pray for godly unity within the Nicaraguan churches. *See Philippians 2:2–3*

> Population: 5,570,129
> Capital: Managua
> Language: Spanish
> Literacy: 68%
> Income (GDP) per capita: $2,400
> Religions: Roman Catholic 73%, evangelical 15%,
>   none 9%, Moravian 2%, other 1%

North Korea

A country where human rights are largely nonexistent and the economy is in long-term failure, North Korea is run by a communist dictator. Many in the country face serious malnutrition. Thousands of Christians have been murdered in the past few decades, and most remaining Christians must worship the Lord in secrecy and at great risk. Evangelism is illegal. **PRAY** for the countless North Koreans suffering from hunger. Pray for the protection of Christians forced to worship in secrecy. Pray that those living in darkness in North Korea would see the great light of the Gospel. *See Matthew 4:16*

> Population: 23,113,019
> Capital: Pyongyang
> Language: Korean
> Literacy: 99%
> Income (GDP) per capita: $1,800
> Religions: Atheism, Buddhism, Confucianism

All the nations you have made will come and worship before you.

—PSALM 86:9

Christ *Jesus*, who died—more than that, who was raised to life—is at the right hand of God and is also interceding for us.

. . . . .

Therefore he is able to save completely those who come to God through him, because he always lives to intercede for them.

—ROMANS 8:34; HEBREWS 7:25

SUNDAY
Pray from 1 Corinthians 9

Prayer Concerns

Answers

MONDAY
1 Corinthians 10:1–18

TUESDAY
1 Corinthians 10:19–33

WHEN PRAYER SEEMS TO GO NOWHERE, SEE PAGE 36

WEDNESDAY

1 Corinthians 11:1–16

Prayer Concerns   *Answers*

THURSDAY

1 Corinthians 11:17–34

FRIDAY

1 Corinthians 12

SATURDAY

1 Corinthians 13

Many may ask, "Is there no other way to pray except through Jesus Christ?" You may pray, but according to the Bible, "*There is ... one mediator between God and men, the man Christ Jesus*" (see 1 Timothy 2:5).

—BILLY GRAHAM

Pray for us. ... May the God of *Peace*, who through the blood of the eternal covenant brought back from the dead our Lord Jesus, that great Shepherd of the sheep, equip you with everything good for doing his will, and may he work in us what is pleasing to him, through Jesus Christ, to whom be glory for ever and ever. Amen.

—HEBREWS 13:18, 20—21

SUNDAY
Pray from 1 Corinthians 14:1–20

Prayer Concerns

Answers

MONDAY
1 Corinthians 14:21–40

TUESDAY
1 Corinthians 15:1–28

WEDNESDAY
1 Corinthians 15:29–58

Prayer Concerns

Answers

THURSDAY
1 Corinthians 16

FRIDAY
2 Corinthians 1

SATURDAY
2 Corinthians 2

Prayer couples you with God's true purposes for you and the world. It not only brings the blessings of God's will to your own personal life, but it brings you the added blessing of being in step with God's plan.

—BILLY GRAHAM

We constantly *Pray* for you, that our God may
count you worthy of his calling, and that by his power
he may fulfill every good purpose of yours and every
act prompted by your faith. We pray this so that the name
of our Lord Jesus may be glorified in you, and you
in him, according to the grace of our God and the
Lord Jesus Christ.

—2 THESSALONIANS 1:11—12

SUNDAY
Pray from 2 Corinthians 3

Prayer Concerns

Answers

MONDAY
2 Corinthians 4

TUESDAY
2 Corinthians 5

WEDNESDAY
2 Corinthians 6

Prayer Concerns

Answers

THURSDAY
2 Corinthians 7

FRIDAY
2 Corinthians 8

SATURDAY
2 Corinthians 9

Above all, be sure that your motive in praying is to glorify God. Our Lord said to His disciples, *"And whatsoever ye shall ask in my name, that will I do, that the Father may be glorified in the Son"* (John 14:13, KJV).

—BILLY GRAHAM

I *Urge*, then, first of all, that requests, prayers, intercession and thanksgiving be made for everyone—for kings and all those in authority, that we may live peaceful and quiet lives in all godliness and holiness. This is good, and pleases God our Savior.

—1 TIMOTHY 2:1–3

SUNDAY
Pray from 2 Corinthians 10

Prayer Concerns　　　　　　　　　　　*Answers*

MONDAY
2 Corinthians 11:1–15

TUESDAY
2 Corinthians 11:16–33

WEDNESDAY
2 Corinthians 12

THURSDAY
2 Corinthians 13

FRIDAY
Galatians 1

SATURDAY
Galatians 2

Today the world is being carried on a rushing torrent of history that is sweeping out of control. There is but one power available to redeem the course of events, and that is the power of prayer by God-fearing, Christ-believing men and women.

—BILLY GRAHAM

PRAY FOR PANAMA

Panama is a country that honors its rich ethnic diversity. The majority of Panamanians are *mestizo* (mixed European and indigenous ancestry), but distinct communities of Spanish, African, West Indian, and Chinese descent also thrive, along with several indigenous ethnic peoples. More than 65,000 students attend the University of Panama, the Technological University, and the University of Santa Maria La Antigua. **PRAY** for those engaged in outreach and ministry to students. Pray that Christian students themselves will live and speak their witness. Pray that the Lord will raise up a passionate young generation who will proclaim His Name to all of Panama. *See Psalm 22:30*

> Population: 3,191,319
> Capital: Panama City
> Languages: Spanish, English
> Literacy: 93%
> Income (GDP) per capita: $7,100
> Religions: Roman Catholic 85%, Protestant 15%

PARAGUAY

The great majority of Paraguayans are baptized Catholics, although many also dabble in occult and animistic practices. A cycle of political instability, regional wars, military governments, and economic isolation has produced endemic corruption affecting every aspect of society. While Protestant churches are steadily growing, they are generally small and divided among at least 33 denominational groupings. Evangelistic outreaches by Franklin Graham and others have been heavily attended, and many have professed faith in Christ. **PRAY** for the new believers in Paraguay and for increased unity among churches. Pray for nominal Catholics to encounter a personal relationship with Jesus Christ. *See Colossians 2:6–10*

> Population: 6,506,464
> Capital: Asunción
> Languages: Spanish, Guaraní
> Literacy: 94%
> Income (GDP) per capita: $4,900
> Religions: Roman Catholic 90%, Protestant 10%

People's Republic of China

While it is nearly impossible to develop reliable statistics about religion in this officially atheistic nation, Christianity has been spreading rapidly in mainland China, whether through the vast network of underground churches or through the witness of churches permitted to worship openly. Even though opposition to Christianity and persecution of converts is a frequent reality of life, Chinese Christians quietly engage in energetic evangelism. **PRAY** for God's protection upon Chinese home churches. Pray for the courage of believers in the face of official opposition. Pray for the more than 1.25 billion Chinese who have not yet heard the Gospel. *See Revelation 3:8*

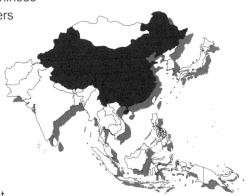

> Population: 1,313,973,713
> Capital: Beijing
> Languages: Chinese, Cantonese,
>   Shanghaiese
> Literacy: 86%
> Income (GDP) per capita: $6,300
> Religions: Officially atheist; Daoist, Buddhist

Peru

With its rich Inca heritage, Peru has a prominent role in South American history. The country stretches from Pacific coastlands east through the Andes Mountains to the tropical Amazon river basin. Land reforms, political upheaval, drug trafficking, failed economic initiatives, and corruption have created an environment where many who feel discouraged and helpless about their society are receptive to the claims of Christ. Churches are growing steadily. **PRAY** for the large population of Quechua (indigenous peoples) and *mestizos* (people of mixed ancestry) from lower- and middle-class backgrounds, who are especially open to the Gospel at this time. *See Matthew 5:3*

> Population: 28,302,603
> Capital: Lima
> Languages: Spanish, Quéchua
> Literacy: 91%
> Income (GDP) per capita: $6,100
> Religions: Roman Catholic 81%, other 19%

All the nations you have made will come and worship before you.
—Psalm 86:9

When I *Heard* these things, I sat down and
wept. For some days I mourned and fasted and prayed
before the God of heaven. Then I said: "O Lord,
God of heaven, the great and awesome God, who keeps
his covenant of love with those who love him and obey
his commands, let your ear be attentive and your eyes
open to hear the prayer your servant is praying before
you day and night."

—NEHEMIAH 1:4—6

SUNDAY
Pray from Galatians 3

Prayer Concerns   *Answers*

MONDAY
Galatians 4

TUESDAY
Galatians 5

WEDNESDAY
Galatians 6

Prayer Concerns

Answers

THURSDAY
Ephesians 1

FRIDAY
Ephesians 2

SATURDAY
Ephesians 3

From one end of the Bible to the other, there is the record of those whose prayers have been answered—men and women who turned the tide of history by prayer; men and women who fervently prayed, and God answered.

—BILLY GRAHAM

Now to him who is *Able* to do immeasurably
more than all we ask or imagine, according to his power
that is at work within us, to him be glory in the church
and in Christ Jesus throughout all generations,
for ever and ever! Amen.

—EPHESIANS 3:20–21

SUNDAY
Pray from Ephesians 4

Prayer Concerns

Answers

MONDAY
Ephesians 5:1–16

TUESDAY
Ephesians 5:17–33

WEDNESDAY
Ephesians 6

Prayer Concerns

Answers

THURSDAY
Philippians 1

FRIDAY
Philippians 2

SATURDAY
Philippians 3

In this modern age in which we live, we have learned to harness the power of the atom, but very few of us have learned how to develop fully the power of prayer. We have not yet learned that we are more powerful on our knees than behind the most powerful weapons that can be developed.

—BILLY GRAHAM

Jesus told his disciples a parable to show them
that they should always pray and not give up.
.....
The Lord said, "... And will not God bring about
justice for his chosen ones, who cry out to him day
and night? Will he keep putting them off?"

—LUKE 18:1, 6—7

SUNDAY
Pray from Philippians 4

Prayer Concerns   *Answers*

MONDAY
Colossians 1

TUESDAY
Colossians 2

WEDNESDAY
Colossians 3

THURSDAY
Colossians 4

FRIDAY
1 Thessalonians 1

SATURDAY
1 Thessalonians 2

How little perseverance and persistence and pleading we show. Some time ago the newspapers told of a man in Washington who spent 17 years securing favorable action on a claim of $81,000 against the government. Yet many people will not pray 17 minutes for the welfare of their own immortal souls or the salvation of other people.

—BILLY GRAHAM

And this is my prayer: that your *Love* may abound more and more in knowledge and depth of insight, so that you may be able to discern what is best and may be pure and blameless until the day of Christ, filled with the fruit of righteousness that comes through Jesus Christ—to the glory and praise of God.

—PHILIPPIANS 1:9–11

SUNDAY
Pray from 1 Thessalonians 3

Prayer Concerns

Answers

MONDAY
1 Thessalonians 4

TUESDAY
1 Thessalonians 5

WEDNESDAY
2 Thessalonians 1

Prayer Concerns   *Answers*

THURSDAY
2 Thessalonians 2

FRIDAY
2 Thessalonians 3

SATURDAY
1 Timothy 1

A life taught in the Scriptures, and tuned in to God in prayer, produces an outflowing of grace and power.

—BILLY GRAHAM

Pray for Philippines

A few years ago, the Philippines became the 20ᵗʰ country to participate in the Billy Graham Evangelistic Association's *My Hope* project. More than 115,000 Christian families across the nation, representing 21,000 local churches, invited friends and neighbors into their homes to watch TV presentations prepared by BGEA especially for Filipino audiences. Participating churches and ministries documented over 200,000 commitments to Jesus Christ through this outreach. This followed outdoor evangelistic meetings in Manila led by Franklin Graham, attended by 317,000 people. **PRAY** that all of those who made decisions for Christ would be discipled by a local church and encouraged and strengthened in their faith. *See Acts 16:5*

> Population: 89,468,677
>
> Capital: Manila
>
> Languages: Filipino, English
>
> Literacy: 96%
>
> Income (GDP) per capita: $5,100
>
> Religions: Roman Catholic 81%, Protestant 8%,
>   Islam 5%, other 6%

Romania

Among the poorest European countries, Romania is one of the richest spiritually. After the upheavals that followed the fall of communism, a growing strength and unity among Christians in Romania has resulted in the number of Protestant churches doubling in a decade. Romania is still emerging from a terrible cultural heritage of parents abandoning children to orphanages. **PRAY** for the churches and Christian ministries at work in orphanages demonstrating the love of Christ. Pray that Romanian young people who grew up abandoned by their parents would experience the healing, life-changing love of their heavenly Father. *See James 1:27*

> Population: 22,303,552
>
> Capital: Bucharest
>
> Language: Romanian
>
> Literacy: 98%
>
> Income (GDP) per capita: $8,400
>
> Religions: Romanian Orthodox 87%,
>   Protestant 8%, Roman Catholic 5%

Russia

Islamic extremists in the Russian Republic of Chechnya continue to wage a war against Russia for independence. The war has thus far been marked with violent acts of terrorism, claiming the lives of many innocent civilians. Despite widespread evangelistic work and missionary efforts since the breakup of the Soviet Union, much of Russia is still considered unreached for Christ. **PRAY** for a peaceful end to the Chechen war and for the many families who have lost loved ones. Pray that the light of the Gospel would dawn on Russians that they might know salvation and peace in Christ. *See Psalm 46:9–10*

> Population: 142,893,540
> Capital: Moscow
> Language: Russian
> Literacy: 100%
> Income (GDP) per capita: $10,700
> Religions: Russian Orthodox 18%,
>   Islam 13%, Protestant 2%, other 67%

Saudi Arabia

Saudi Arabia, Islam's country of origin, forbids Christians to worship together or own a Bible. Most of the few Christians in the country are foreigners, such as contract laborers from Asia. Christian missionaries are strictly forbidden, and anyone who shares the truths of Christ with a Muslim does so at the risk of arrest or death. Muslims who convert to Christianity are subject to imprisonment or execution. **PRAY** that God will give the few Saudi Arabian Christians a spirit of courage and wisdom. Pray that God will open the eyes of Muslims in Saudi Arabia to the truths of Jesus Christ. *See Acts 26:18*

> Population: 27,019,731
> Capital: Riyadh
> Language: Arabic
> Literacy: 79%
> Income (GDP) per capita: $12,900
> Religion: Islam 100%

All the nations you have made will come and worship before you.
—Psalm 86:9

Peter sent them *All* out of the room; then he
got down on his knees and prayed.

—ACTS 9:40

SUNDAY
Pray from 1 Timothy 2

Prayer Concerns

Answers

MONDAY
1 Timothy 3

TUESDAY
1 Timothy 4

HELPS FOR YOUR TIME ALONE WITH GOD, SEE PAGE 13

WEDNESDAY
1 Timothy 5

Prayer Concerns   *Answers*

THURSDAY
1 Timothy 6

FRIDAY
2 Timothy 1

SATURDAY
2 Timothy 2

Our Lord frequently prayed alone, separating Himself from every earthly distraction.
I would strongly urge you to select a room or corner in your home or in your yard where
you, alone, can regularly meet God.

—BILLY GRAHAM

But I tell you who hear me: *Love* your enemies, do good to those who hate you, bless those who curse you, pray for those who mistreat you.

—LUKE 6:27–28

SUNDAY
Pray from 2 Timothy 3

Prayer Concerns

Answers

MONDAY
2 Timothy 4

TUESDAY
Titus 1

WEDNESDAY
Titus 2

THURSDAY
Titus 3

FRIDAY
Philemon

SATURDAY
Hebrews 1

How startling His instructions and His example. He tells us to "pray for them which despitefully use you, and persecute you." In other words, He says to pray for your enemies. How many of us have ever spent time praying for our enemies?

—BILLY GRAHAM

All that belongs to the *Father* is mine. That is
why I said the Spirit will take from what is mine and
make it known to you. ... I tell you the truth, my
Father will give you whatever you ask in my name. Until
now you have not asked for anything in my name.
Ask and you will receive, and your joy will be complete.

—JOHN 16:15, 23—24

SUNDAY
Pray from Hebrews 2

Prayer Concerns

Answers

MONDAY
Hebrews 3

TUESDAY
Hebrews 4

ASK THE HOLY SPIRIT TO GUIDE YOUR PRAYING (ROMANS 8:26—27)

WEDNESDAY
Hebrews 5

Prayer Concerns   *Answers*

THURSDAY
Hebrews 6

FRIDAY
Hebrews 7

SATURDAY
Hebrews 8

The Scripture says that the one mediator between God and us is Jesus Christ. You must know Him, and you must pray in His Name. Your prayers must be directed according to the will of God, and the Holy Spirit will do that for you.

—BILLY GRAHAM

The Lord is *Close* to the brokenhearted
and saves those who are crushed in spirit.

. . . . .

[Jesus] began to teach them, saying: "Blessed are the poor
in spirit, for theirs is the kingdom of heaven."

—PSALM 34:18; MATTHEW 5:2—3

SUNDAY
Pray from Hebrews 9

Prayer Concerns   *Answers*

MONDAY
Hebrews 10:1—18

TUESDAY
Hebrews 10:19—39

WHEN IT SEEMS GOD ISN'T LISTENING, SEE PAGE 36

WEDNESDAY
Hebrews 11:1–19

Prayer Concerns   *Answers*

THURSDAY
Hebrews 11:20–40

FRIDAY
Hebrews 12

SATURDAY
Hebrews 13

The mourning of inadequacy is a weeping that catches the attention of God.
The Bible says, *"The Lord is nigh unto them that are of a broken heart; and
saveth such as be of a contrite spirit"* (Psalm 34:18, KJV).

—BILLY GRAHAM

Pray for Sri Lanka

While the majority of people in Sri Lanka are Buddhist, many have become open to the Good News of Jesus in recent years. In response, Buddhist leaders have pushed for legislation to restrict church construction and make it illegal to lead a Buddhist to Christ. There are currently 35,000 villages in Sri Lanka that have had no active witness to the Gospel. **PRAY** that Christians in Sri Lanka would boldly proclaim the Gospel without fear. Pray that God will send forth many with a passion to proclaim the peace and salvation found in Christ to their countrymen who have never heard. *See Isaiah 52:7*

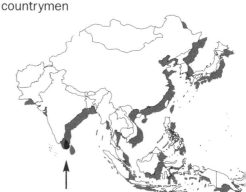

    Population: 20,222,240

    Capital: Colombo

    Languages: Sinhala, Tamil

    Literacy: 92%

    Income (GDP) per capita: $4,300

    Religions: Buddhist 70%, Islam 8%,
       Hindu 7%, Christian 6%, other 9%

Sudan

The Sudanese government and radical Islamic militia groups have waged war on civilians in the south of Sudan for many years, and in the western Darfur region since 2003. In Darfur alone, the violence has claimed over 400,000 civilian lives, with even larger numbers of refugees. In the south where fighting has waned, Samaritan's Purse has launched a plan to rebuild hundreds of churches burned or bombed during years of attacks. **PRAY** that the Lord will bring justice for all who are oppressed in Sudan. Pray that the rebuilt churches will be filled with worshipers who bring glory to Christ's Name. *See Haggai 1:8*

    Population: 41,236,378

    Capital: Khartoum

    Language: Arabic

    Literacy: 61%

    Income (GDP) per capita: $2,100

    Religions: Islam (Sunni) 70%,
       Indigenous 25%, Christian 5%

Tajikistan

The majority of Tajiks are Muslim, many of whom mix local superstitions with Islamic beliefs. There are about a quarter million citizens of Christian heritage, mostly Russian or Ukrainian Orthodox, but many who acknowledge this affiliation do so largely to maintain their cultural identity. Evangelism is closely monitored and often repressed by the authorities. Nevertheless, in the past 15 years, the number of practicing Christians has increased. **PRAY** for evangelists and pastors who have come from other Asian nations, such as Korea, to serve in Tajikistan. Pray that Tajik Christians will be enabled to proclaim the Gospel with or without interference. *See Ephesians 6:19*

- Population: 7,320,815
- Capital: Dushanbe
- Languages: Tajik, Russian
- Literacy: $1,200
- Income (GDP) per capita: $2,100
- Religions: Islam 90% (Sunni 85%, Shiite 5%), other 10%

Thailand

Buddhism is closely connected with the Thai sense of national identity, making evangelism difficult. Recent economic struggles, however, have brought more openness in the hearts of many people. The Thai government allows freedom of religion. Teaching English has proved to be an effective way to reach Thai people for Christ. Of the Muslims in Thailand, 90 percent are immigrants or workers from Malaysia. Some observers consider this one of the largest reachable Muslim communities in the world. **PRAY** that God will open effective evangelistic outreach among Malaysian workers in Thailand. Pray that the Lord will establish the Thai people's identity in Himself. *See Isaiah 65:1*

- Population: 64,631,595
- Capital: Bangkok
- Languages: Thai, English
- Literacy: 96%
- Income (GDP) per capita: $8,300
- Religions: Buddhist 95%, Islam 5%

All the nations you have made will come and worship before you.
—Psalm 86:9

Yet [Abraham] did not *Waver* through unbelief
regarding the promise of God, but was strengthened in
his faith and gave glory to God, being fully persuaded
that God had power to do what he had promised. This is
why "it was credited to him as righteousness."

—ROMANS 4:20–22

SUNDAY
Pray from James 1

Prayer Concerns

Answers

MONDAY
James 2

TUESDAY
James 3

WEDNESDAY
James 4

Prayer Concerns   *Answers*

THURSDAY
James 5

FRIDAY
1 Peter 1

SATURDAY
1 Peter 2

Faith pleases God more than anything else. The Christian life is dependent upon faith. We stand on faith; we live on faith; we pray in faith. Faith is loved and honored by God more than any other single thing.

—BILLY GRAHAM

"For *My* thoughts are not your thoughts,
neither are your ways my ways," declares the Lord.
.....
"I am the Lord; in its time I will do this swiftly."

—ISAIAH 55:8; 60:22

SUNDAY
Pray from 1 Peter 3

Prayer Concerns   *Answers*

MONDAY
1 Peter 4

TUESDAY
1 Peter 5

PRAYING WHEN THE ANSWER SEEMS LONG-DELAYED, SEE PAGE 48

WEDNESDAY
1 Peter 1

THURSDAY
1 Peter 2

FRIDAY
1 Peter 3

SATURDAY
1 John 1

God knows what is best for us, and sometimes His answer to our prayers is "No" or "Not yet." But that shouldn't keep us from praying! God loves us, and He can be trusted to do what is best. The Bible tells us to *"pray continually"* (1 Thessalonians 5:17).

—BILLY GRAHAM

Pray in the *Spirit* on all occasions with all kinds of prayers and requests. With this in mind, be alert and always keep on praying for all the saints. Pray also for me.

—EPHESIANS 6:18—19

SUNDAY
Pray from 1 John 2

Prayer Concerns   *Answers*

MONDAY
1 John 3

TUESDAY
1 John 4

WEDNESDAY
1 John 5

Prayer Concerns   *Answers*

THURSDAY
2 John

FRIDAY
3 John

SATURDAY
Jude

That "the Spirit Himself makes intercession" (see Romans 8:26) indicates that it is actually God pleading, praying, and mourning through us. Thus we become co-laborers with God, actual partners with Him (see 2 Corinthians 6:1); our lives are lifted from the low plane of selfishness to the high plane of creativeness with God.

—BILLY GRAHAM

Then (*Jesus*) said to them: "Nation will rise against nation, and kingdom against kingdom. There will be great earthquakes, famines and pestilences in various places, and fearful events and great signs from heaven. ... When these things begin to take place, stand up and lift up your heads, because your redemption is drawing near."

—LUKE 21:10—11, 28

SUNDAY
Pray from Revelation 1

Prayer Concerns

Answers

MONDAY
Revelation 2

TUESDAY
Revelation 3

WEDNESDAY
Revelation 4

Prayer Concerns

Answers

THURSDAY
Revelation 5

FRIDAY
Revelation 6

SATURDAY
Revelation 7

In the middle of our world troubles the Christian is not to go about wringing his hands, shouting: "What shall we do?" and having more nervous tension and worry than anyone else. The Christian is to trust quietly that God is still on the throne. He is a Sovereign God, working out things according to His own plan.

—BILLY GRAHAM

Pray for Ukraine

The number of evangelical churches in the Ukraine has more than doubled since emerging from communist rule. New believers are very zealous in sharing their faith in Christ with others. The rapid growth of the Ukrainian church has led to a great need for pastors and other Christian leaders to shepherd these young Christians. **PRAY** that the Ukrainian church will continue to grow in numbers and maturity. Pray for spiritual renewal in Ukrainian Orthodox and Ukrainian Greek churches. Pray that the Lord will raise up leaders in the Ukraine to shepherd His people. *See Ephesians 4:11–13*

Population: 46,710,816

Capital: Kiev

Languages: Ukrainian, Russian

Literacy: 100%

Income (GDP) per capita: $6,800

Religions: Ukrainian Orthodox 44%,
   Ukrainian Greek Catholic 6%, other 50%

United Kingdom

While committed believers live, worship, and serve throughout the United Kingdom, secularism and false doctrine have seeped into the Church. Many who profess to be Christians do not hold to the basic biblical truths on which Christianity is founded. It is no surprise, therefore, that the number of those active in church has dropped dramatically in a nation which was once known for worldwide Christian leadership and outreach. **PRAY** for repentance and revival to come upon the United Kingdom. *See Hebrews 4:12*

Population: 60,609,153

Capital: London

Languages: English, Welsh, Scots Gaelic

Literacy: 99%

Income (GDP) per capita: $30,900

Religions: Christian 72%, Muslim 3%,
   other 25%

VENEZUELA

is estimated that more than half of Venezuelans live in poverty despite a socialist economy supported by oil exports. Many who call themselves Catholic still dabble actively in occult practices. In recent years, expatriate Christian missionaries have been restricted or forced out by the government. Nevertheless, there is great openness to the Gospel, and the number of evangelical Christians has increased dramatically in just a few years. **PRAY** that those involved with occult practices will forsake their idols and turn their hearts fully to the Lord. Pray that the Church will continue to grow and mature in the Lord. *See Ezekiel 14:6*

Population: 25,730,435
Capital: Caracas
Language: Spanish
Literacy: 93%
Income (GDP) per capita: $6,500
Religions: Roman Catholic 88%,
    Protestant 10%, other 2%

YEMEN

Regarded as the home of the Queen of Sheba, Yemen is a religiously closed country where it is illegal to share the Gospel with a Muslim or for a Muslim to convert to Christianity. It is considered one of the least evangelized countries on earth. **PRAY** that the Lord, in His great mercy, will send forth His Word to those in Yemen, opening doors for a witness despite the powerful obstacles. Ask the Lord to call individual Christians in many countries to pray regularly for a breakthrough in Yemen. *See Isaiah 9:2*

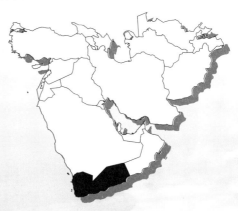

Population: 21,456,188
Capital: Sanaá
Language: Arabic
Literacy: 50%
Income (GDP) per capita: $800
Religion: Islam 100%

All the nations you have made will come and worship before you.
—PSALM 86:9

Search me, O God, and know my *Heart*;
test me and know my anxious thoughts. See if there is
any offensive way in me, and lead me in the way everlasting.

—PSALM 139:23—24

SUNDAY
Pray from Revelation 8

Prayer Concerns   *Answers*

MONDAY
Revelation 9

TUESDAY
Revelation 10

WEDNESDAY
Revelation 11

Prayer Concerns

Answers

THURSDAY
Revelation 12

FRIDAY
Revelation 13

SATURDAY
Revelation 14

Get on your knees before God and ask Him if there are any areas of your life that are still unyielded to Him. The searchlight of His Spirit will probe the inner depths of your soul and reveal things that you think you have already yielded, but you have not.

—BILLY GRAHAM

Forget the former things; do not dwell on the past. See, I am doing a new thing! Now it springs up; do you not perceive it?

—ISAIAH 43:18—19

SUNDAY
Pray from Revelation 15–16

Prayer Concerns

Answers

MONDAY
Revelation 17

TUESDAY
Revelation 18

WEDNESDAY
Revelation 19

Prayer Concerns   *Answers*

THURSDAY
Revelation 20

FRIDAY
Revelation 21

SATURDAY
Revelation 22

You were created in the image and likeness of God. You were made for God's fellowship and your heart can never be satisfied without His communion. Let your prayer be like that of the psalmist, *"Oh, God, thou art my God; early will I seek thee: my soul thirsteth for thee, my flesh longeth for thee in a dry and thirsty land, where no water is"* (Psalm 63:1, KJV).

—BILLY GRAHAM

Remember the Other Nations

The worldwide family of nations is nearly 200-strong. Space allows the inclusion of only 52 of those nations in this volume. The following were not included, but deserve a place in our prayers.

Afghanistan	Djibouti
Albania	Dominica
Algeria	Dominican Republic
Andorra	East Timor
Angola	Equatorial Guinea
Antigua and Barbuda	Eritrea
Azerbaijan	Ethiopia
Bahamas, The	Fiji
Bahrain	Finland
Barbados	Gabon
Belize	Germany
Bermuda	Ghana
Bhutan	Greenland
Botswana	Grenada
Brazil	Guinea
Brunei	Guinea-Bissau
Bulgaria	Guyana
Burkina Faso	Hungary
Burundi	Iceland
Cambodia	Indonesia
Cameroon	Ireland
Cape Verde	Italy
Central African Republic	Jamaica
Chad	Jordan
Comoros	Kazakhstan
Congo, Democratic Republic of the	Kenya
Congo, Republic of the	Kiribati
Cote d'Ivoire	Korea, South
Croatia	Kuwait
Cuba	Kyrgyzstan
Cyprus	Laos
Denmark	Latvia

Lebanon
Lesotho
Liberia
Libya
Liechtenstein
Lithuania
Luxembourg
Macedonia
Madagascar
Malawi
Malaysia
Maldives
Malta
Marshall Islands
Mauritania
Mauritius
Micronesia, Federated States of
Monaco
Montenegro
Morocco
Mozambique
Namibia
Nauru
Nepal
New Zealand
Niger
Nigeria
Norway
Oman
Pakistan
Palau
Papua New Guinea
Poland
Portugal
Qatar
Rwanda
Saint Kitts and Nevis
Saint Lucia

Saint Vincent and the Grenadines
Samoa
San Marino
Sao Tome and Principe
Senegal
Serbia
Seychelles
Sierra Leone
Singapore
Slovakia
Slovenia
Solomon Islands
Somalia
South Africa
Spain
Suriname
Svalbard
Swaziland
Sweden
Switzerland
Syria
Tanzania
Togo
Tonga
Trinidad and Tobago
Tunisia
Turkey
Turkmenistan
Tuvalu
Uganda
United Arab Emirates
Uruguay
Uzbekistan
Vanuatu
Vietnam
Zambia
Zimbabwe

All the nations you have made will come and worship before you.

—PSALM 86:9

Sources

Prayer, by Billy Graham, is excerpted and updated from a sermon classic ©1955 (renewed 1983, revised 1993, 1994, 2001, 2005, 2006) Billy Graham Evangelistic Association.

Have a Vital Time Alone With God is excerpted from *A Biblical Standard for Evangelists*, presented by Billy Graham at a conference in Amsterdam, The Netherlands, July 1983, ©1984 Billy Graham Evangelistic Association.

A Powerful Way to Pray God's Word, by Robert J. Morgan, was originally published in *Christian Reader* magazine, July 1999, under the title *What Ruth Graham Taught Me About Prayer: A powerful way to make God's words your own* ©Robert J. Morgan, used by permission. Rob Morgan is a pastor in Nashville, Tennessee.

Quotations on pages 4, 16, 22, 29, 31, 43, 45, 48, 55, 57, 59, 65, 67, 69, 73, 75, 83, 85, 93, and 145 are from Billy Graham's *My Answer* syndicated newspaper columns, various dates, used by permission.

Quotations on pages 21, 27, 39, 99, 103, 105, 107, 109, 113, 115, 117, 119, 123, 125, 127, 133, 135, 137, 149, and 153 are from Billy Graham sermon collections, various dates, ©Billy Graham Evangelistic Association.

Quotations on pages 19, 41, 53, 87, 89, 95, 97, 139, 143, 147, and 155 are from *Day by Day With Billy Graham* by Billy Graham, ©1976 Billy Graham Evangelistic Association.

Quotations on pages 33 and 129 are from *A Biblical Standard for Evangelists* by Billy Graham ©1984 Billy Graham Evangelistic Association.

Quotation on page 36 is from *Just As I Am* by Billy Graham ©1997 Billy Graham Evangelistic Association.

Quotations on pages 63, 77, 79, and back cover are from public comments by Billy Graham. (The quotation on page 79 and back cover alludes to a statement that originated with Cameron V. Thompson.)

Countries of the world information from BGEA research